GW00838398

STUFFED*

POSITIVE ACTION GLOBAL
TO PREVENT A
FOOD CRISIS

Design: Jodie Inkson
at Wire Sky www.wiresky.co.uk
Text: Pat Thomas
Text (Chapter 4):
Rikke Bruntse-Dahl
Editor: Emily Walmsley
Project Manager: Lyn Hemming
Production: Julia Richardson

First edition of Stuffed
Copyright February 2010
Alastair Sawday Publishing Co. Ltd
Text copyright Pat Thomas
and The Soil Association
Fragile Earth an imprint of
Alastair Sawday Publishing Co. Ltd
Published in 2010
Alastair Sawday Publishing Co. Ltd
The Old Farmyard, Yanley Lane,
Long Ashton, Bristol BS41 9LR
Tel: +44 (0)1275 395430
Fax: +44 (0)1275 393388
Email: info@sawdays.co.uk
or info@fragile-earth.com
Web: www.sawdays.co.uk
or www.fragile-earth.com

All rights reserved. No part of this
publication may be used other
than for the purpose for which
it is intended nor may any part
be reproduced, or transmitted,
in any form or by any means,
electronically or mechanically,
including photocopying, recording
or any storage or retrieval system
without prior written permission
from the publisher. Request for
permission should be addressed
to Alastair Sawday Publishing
Co. Ltd.

A catalogue record for this book
is available from the British Library.
This publication is not included
under licences issued by the
Copyright Agency. No part of
this publication may be used
in any form of advertising, sales
promotion or publicity.

The publishers have made every
effort to ensure the accuracy of the
information in this book at the time
of going to press. However, they
cannot accept any responsibility
for any loss, injury or inconvenience
resulting from the use of information
contained therein. They have also
made every effort to acknowledge
information and obtain permissions.
Any omissions notified will be
corrected in subsequent editions
of this work.

ISBN-13: 978-1-906136-47-5
Printed in Frome by Butler Tanner
& Dennis

Special thanks go to Tim Young
and Roger Mortlock at the
Soil Association, Mairi McLellan
at Wire Sky, Barbara Westmore,
Rosemary Anderson, to all the
essay authors and to the team
at Ecotricity.

CONTENTS

HOW CAN YOU TAKE AVOID THE GLOBAI

THE COMBINATION OF CLIMATE CHANGE, RESOURCE DEPLETION AND POPULATION GROWTH HAS BEEN CALLED 'THE PERFECT STORM'. IN THE NEXT 10–20 YEARS THESE CHALLENGES WILL FORCE US RADICALLY TO RETHINK THE WAY WE LIVE OUR LIVES. PERHAPS THE MOST FUNDAMENTAL CHANGE WILL BE IN OUR RELATIONSHIP WITH FOOD. OVER THE PAST 60 YEARS OUR CONNECTION WITH FOOD AND HOW IT'S PRODUCED HAS BECOME INCREASINGLY DISLOCATED. FOOD HAS BECOME A COMMODITY. OUR CURRENT INTENSIVE, INDUSTRIAL MODEL BASED ON HIGH INPUTS OF FOSSIL FUEL, GLOBAL SOURCING AND CENTRALISED DISTRIBUTION IS NEITHER SUSTAINABLE NOR RESILIENT AGAINST FUTURE SHOCKS.

This book proves there is another way. It includes essays from some of the world's most forward-thinking writers on food and farming, who describe the seriousness of the food crisis facing us. But it's also a handbook of solutions. When the Soil Association was founded in 1946, its aim was to create a movement of informed citizens who understood the connection between the health of food, people and the planet. Now that mission is more important than ever and reading this book will explain why. It also describes what you can do – in your kitchen, in your garden, in your community and as a citizen of the world. Issues like climate change and peak oil can sometimes make us feel powerless; but food is different. Wendell Berry called eating an 'agricultural act' and it's true: we can all do something to change our relationship with food.

DIRECT ACTION TO FOOD CRISIS? PATRICK HOLDEN

This book is for anyone who cares about the future of food. Unlike some of the other environmental challenges facing us, transition to a more sustainable food culture is not about giving anything up; it could actually improve the quality of our lives by reconnecting us with what we eat. Already in the UK there is a vibrant movement of food pioneers – farmers, growers, food producers and, of course, those who enjoy good food – who know that change is coming. Vegetable seeds now outsell flower seeds, the 'grow-your-own' bug has gripped the nation, and increasing numbers of people want to know more about where their food comes from.

Rather like animals sensing a tsunami before it arrives, we know that the way we farm, produce and eat food will need to change. At the Soil Association we are working alongside communities around the UK to prove that change is possible. Please look at our website to find out more about how you can join us – and what role you can play in this new food revolution.

Patrick Holden
Director of the Soil Association
www.soilassociation.org
www.stuffedonline.org

THANK YOU!

Stuffed would not have been possible without all the contributors who have given their time and energy to make it happen. Thanks also to The Roddick Foundation and to Susan Robinson, whose generous support has enabled the production of this book. I'd also like to thank our main sponsors on this project – Ecotricity, the UK's first green electricity company who have now become the established name in renewable energy supplies for households across the UK and are long-term supporters of the Soil Association.

 Soil Association   ecotricity

A SHORT WORD
with Michael Pollan

Author of the prize-winning *The Omnivore's Dilemma*
(2007) and contributing author to *Food, INC* (2009)

PREFACE

I SUSPECT THAT READING THIS BOOK WILL COMPLICATE YOUR EATING LIFE. LUCKILY, IT WILL BE WORTH IT, AS THERE ARE STILL PLENTY OF GOOD THINGS OUT THERE TO EAT. BY GOOD I MEAN NOT ONLY DELICIOUS AND HEALTHY (GOOD FOR US) BUT ALSO GOOD FOR THE WORLD – FOR THE ENVIRONMENT, FOR THE WORKERS WHO PRODUCE THE FOOD, AND, IN THE CASE OF MEAT OR DAIRY, FOR THE ANIMALS.

My family eats much less meat than we used to, and when we do eat it, we buy it from farms, ranches or companies we know enough about to trust. We only eat grass-fed beef, which we can buy in local markets if not directly from a rancher. In the case of plant-based foods, we usually buy organic or local, or ideally both – I think organic fruits and vegetables taste better, and I like the idea that my food cash is supporting farmers who care about the land. We also try to shop at the farmers' market as often as possible. The food there is picked fresh so it's at the peak of its taste and nutritional quality, and every dollar goes directly to the producers.

If this all sounds a lot more trouble than buying whatever's on sale at the supermarket, you're right. It also costs a little more. But I think it's worth it. It's amazing how knowing the story behind your food can make it taste better. (Or, if it's a bad story, worse.) But I also enjoy meeting farmers at the market, and seeing how my food dollars help build a new food chain, one devoted to health at every step: to the health of the land, the health of the plants and animals, the health of my family, and the health of my community.

I call shopping and eating this way 'voting with your fork'. How you and your family choose to spend your food money represents one of the most powerful votes you have.

You can vote to support the kind of feedlot where steer no. 534 spent his miserable life, or you can vote for farms where animals have the lives they were meant to, where the land is healed in the process, and the farmers make a decent living. That kind of alternative farm was created not only by visionary farmers but by visionary consumers like you.

I've never liked to think of myself as a mere 'consumer'. The word makes it sound like someone who uses things up and diminishes the world, which very often is exactly what a consumer does. But a consumer can be a creator too, by using his or her eating choices to help build a new food system. That is a potent vote, and you get three of them every day. Perhaps best of all, when it comes to food, you don't have to wait till you're 18 to have a say. You can have one today, at your next meal.

But how exactly should you fill up your plates? Many people have asked this question so I've developed a handful of everyday rules to guide you through the new-found challenges (and possibilities) of mealtimes.

MY ADVICE COMES IN THREE PARTS:

EAT REAL FOOD

That sounds pretty simple, but it's not so easy to do. There are many things disguised as food in our supermarkets and fast-food restaurants; I call them 'edible food-like substances' (EFLS for short) and suggest you avoid them. But how do you tell the difference between real food and EFLS?

Here are a few rules of thumb:

- Don't eat anything that your great-grandmother wouldn't recognise as food.

  Imagine she's by your side when you're picking up something to eat. Does she have any idea what that squeezable yogurt tube is or how you're supposed to eat it?

- Don't eat anything with more than five ingredients, or with ingredients you don't recognise or can't pronounce.

  That long ingredient list means a highly processed product – an EFLS is likely to contain more sugar, salt and fat than your body needs, and very few real nutrients.

- Don't eat anything containing high-fructose corn syrup.

Think about it: only corporations ever 'cook' with the stuff. Avoid it and you will automatically avoid many of the worst kinds of EFLS, including fizzy drinks.

BUY REAL FOOD

To make sure you buy real food:

- Buy food from the outside perimeter of the supermarket and avoid the middle aisles.

- In the cafeteria, go for the salad bar or fruit basket, where there are still fresh plant and animal foods.

- Don't buy, or eat, anything that doesn't eventually rot.

- A food engineered to live forever is usually full of chemicals. Food should be alive, and that means it should eventually die.

- Shop at the farmers' market, through a box scheme or at your local farm shop.

- Get out of the supermarket, the corner shop and the petrol station, and you won't find those flashy fake foods.

- Be your own food detective.

- Pay attention to where your food comes from (were those berries picked nearby or halfway around the world?) and how it is produced (organic, grass-fed, humanely raised?). Read labels and ask questions.

EAT REAL MEALS

How you prepare and eat food is often just as important as what you eat. So:

Cook
The best way to take control of your meals is to cook whenever you can. As soon as you start cooking, you begin to learn about ingredients, care about their quality and develop your sense of taste. You'll find that fast food becomes boring in comparison – more of the same salty, fatty and sugary taste in every microwave pizza.

Garden
The freshest, best-tasting food you can eat is from the garden. Nothing is more satisfying than to cook and eat food you have grown yourself.

Try not to eat alone
When we eat alone we eat without thinking, and we usually eat too much. Just think how mindlessly you can put away a bag of crisps or cookies in front of the television or computer. Eating should be social; food is more fun when you share it.

Eat slowly – stop when you're full
The food industry makes money by getting you to eat more than you need or want to. Just because a restaurant offers a super-sized burger meal doesn't mean you should eat it. Take back control of your portions.

Eat at the table
We snack more than we dine these days. The deepest joys of eating come when we slow down to savour our food and share it with people we love. The real meal – family and friends gathered around a table – is on the verge of extinction. For the sake of your family's health and happiness, and for your own, do what you can to save it.

"Voting with your fork ~ how you choose to spend your food money represents one of the most powerful votes you have."

STUFFED IF WE DO

STUFFED IF WE DON'T

GET IT RIGHT AND THE GLOBAL POPULATION WILL BE WELL-FED AND HEALTHY, STUFFED FULL OF GOOD FOODS AND SATISFIED. THE EARTH WILL BE BALANCED AND BOUNTIFUL, FULL OF LIFE AND VIBRATING WITH HEALTH...

GET IT WRONG AND STUFFED TAKES ON A WHOLE NEW MEANING. THE PLANET IS IN PERIL, CLIMATE CHANGE RUNS RAMPANT, ECOSYSTEMS ARE DAMAGED BEYOND REPAIR, THERE'S NOT ENOUGH FOOD TO EAT AND THE SURVIVAL OF THE HUMAN SPECIES IS IN DOUBT...

FOOD FOR A

FOOD OCCUPIES A UNIQUE POSITION IN OUR LIVES. IT IS A SOURCE OF NOURISHMENT AND PLEASURE, IT PROVIDES THE GLUE THAT HOLDS FAMILIES TOGETHER AND FORMS THE SCAFFOLDING OF OUR SOCIAL INTERACTIONS. MANY OF US HAVE BEEN PRIVILEGED TO LIVE IN A WORLD WHERE FOOD ISN'T A PROBLEM. WE GO TO THE SUPERMARKET AND THERE IT IS: CHEAP, PLENTIFUL, UNIFORM, CLEAN, PRE-PACKAGED FOOD, NOT LIMITED BY SEASON OR GEOGRAPHICAL DISTANCE.

But, increasingly, all around the world, food is becoming a problem. The food system that seemed miraculously and effortlessly to meet our needs is showing signs of breakdown. It is becoming a political hot potato and an environmental liability. Instead of being associated with unending bounty, food is increasingly linked to words such as scarcity, security and crisis.

The system is in peril because of a complex combination of challenges unique to our time in history: in particular, peak oil and climate change, but also declining water supplies and a growing world population. Too many of us who make the weekly trek to the supermarket are failing to make the link between these globally significant events and their impact on our food supply, and our food supply's impact in exacerbating some of these events. Difficult questions are becoming harder to ignore: What will we eat when these converging crises finally meet? How will the way we grow and sell food have to change? How might our diets need to adapt? How might our relationship to food and farmers evolve? When the oil runs out, where will our coffee, tea, chocolate, bananas, mangoes, out-of-season salad vegetables, cheap meat and freshly squeezed orange juice come from?

EATING OIL

The world draws its energy from fossil fuels and supplies are rapidly diminishing. The chances are that most of us still don't realise that when we eat food we are really eating oil: today's food supply is, in fact, taking a big bite out of tomorrow's carbon energy supply.

Industrial agriculture is an energy-intensive and energy inefficient business. Most of the oil is used up in the production of fertilisers and pesticides, in running large-scale farming operations and in the transport and packaging of goods.

Studies show that it takes between seven and ten calories of fuel to create one calorie of edible food. Of course, this is just an average; some foods, like meat and dairy, are much more energy hungry; it takes, for example, up to 35 calories of fuel for every single calorie of beef produced. All this before we even refrigerate or cook our food at home.

Our insatiable thirst for energy and our demand for the right to travel when and where we like has led to the development of biofuels – derived from food crops and other plant materials. Land that could be used to grow food for people is being diverted to grow food for cars and lorries, which is leading to a scarcity of edible crops, higher food prices and damage to the ecosystem.

In modern agriculture there is also a huge amount of wasteful transport. In the UK, for example, we export nearly twice as much milk as we import. In other words, locally produced milk that could be consumed here is transported elsewhere to increase profits – and inflate prices. Likewise, here in the UK we import 240,000 tonnes of pork and 125,000 tonnes of lamb, while exporting 195,000 tonnes of pork and 102,000 tonnes of lamb. The UK also imports 61,400 tonnes of poultry meat a year from the Netherlands and exports 33,100 tonnes to the Netherlands.

Each of these transactions requires energy, which is both irrational and unsustainable in a world where oil is running out.

The first chapters of this book show how we, as individuals, can stop eating oil – in our kitchens, our gardens, our communities and our schools. Whether it's learning how to identify low-impact foods and integrate them into our family diet; rethinking how to cook and store food from an energy efficiency point of view; learning how to keep chickens or bees; growing our own fruit and vegetables either in our own garden or allotment or as part of a community project; helping to set up a local farmers' market; or teaching the next generation about sustainable food, everyone has a role to play in building more resilient local food systems.

HOTTING UP

Intimately bound up in our profligate energy use is the issue of climate change. Climate change is driven by emissions of greenhouse gases (GHGs) such as carbon dioxide, methane and nitrous oxide. As levels of these GHGs rise, they trap heat in the atmosphere, which in turn changes our climate and weather systems dramatically. Because of man-made climate change, places that were once green farmland have become deserts, places once covered in ice are beginning to melt, and there are more floods and other extreme weather events that have both direct and indirect effects on our food supply.

Most of us associate GHGs with cars and planes, but agriculture and food production, because of their energy-intensive nature, make a big contribution. According to the United Nations, farming is responsible for around 30% of global CO_2 emissions. In other words, intensive agriculture is feeding its own destruction. This is due not only to the large amounts of energy used in processing and transporting food, and the huge demand for fertilisers and pesticides, but also to the destruction of vast swathes of forests in places like the Amazon to make way for farms.

Climate scientists say we must cut our global emissions of GHGs by 80% by 2050 if we are to have any hope of averting the worst impacts of climate change. Some of these are already beginning to affect our food supply.

These impacts are becoming most apparent in the 'monoculture' crop varieties that are bred to produce high yields under very specific conditions of sunlight, temperature and water and with high inputs of fertilisers and pesticides. These varieties are not very adaptable, so when environmental factors start changing, as they are now, they can quickly begin to fail.

Intensive farming can impact the climate in other ways too. For instance, although trees are important carbon sinks, most of the world's carbon is stored in soil. Continually ploughing fields to plant new crops – much of which go to feed farm animals – releases vast amounts of carbon into the atmosphere. In contrast, rotating crops and using pasture grazed by animals to build fertility, keeps the carbon in the ground. Farming in this way could still produce enough quality livestock to meet our needs, while also preserving soil fertility and fighting climate change.

There are now alternative ways of getting food to our tables, as the following chapters on cities, farming and transforming the global food system show. In particular, new agricultural techniques are available which view farms as integrated systems maintaining a healthy soil and reducing greenhouse gas emissions. These work along the principles of producing seasonal, local and organic goods that provide enough nutritious food for everyone, without the need for oil-based fertilisers.

16

WATER CRISIS

Drought conditions in Australia's Murray–Darling basin have reduced a once fertile valley – responsible for 85% of the water used for irrigation in Australia and 40% of the country's grain, fruit and vegetables – into a virtual desert. The drought cut the 2006–07 wheat crop down from 25 million tonnes the previous year to just 9.8 million tonnes and bankrupted its farmers, many of whom had worked the land for generations.

Throughout Asia rice crops are also failing due to prolonged flooding or drought. In rice-producing nations stocks fell in 2008 to their lowest levels for 30 years. This prompted one country, Malaysia, to outrage the international community by opting out of the global marketplace altogether: it offered a simple swap with any country willing to exchange a shipload of palm oil for a shipload of rice.

In 2008, shortages of staple foods triggered riots from western Africa to Mexico, Uzbekistan, Haiti and Egypt, as well as panic buying and violent consumer protests in Europe. According to the United Nations Food and Agriculture Organization, the shortages also plunged an additional 75 million people below the hunger threshold, bringing the total number to around 1.75 billion.

As crop yields decline or become unreliable, the pressure on farmers to grow crops on marginal land increases. But there is a limit to how much land can be pressed into service to produce food without creating more problems. Marginal land is often not 'marginal' at all but has an active role as a refuge for wildlife and as a carbon sink. Using marginal land can require more fertilisers and water to produce the same yields expected from more fertile arable land. This, in turn, can hasten the loss of biodiversity and soil erosion and, of course, diminish that land's role as a carbon sink.

Fresh water supplies, just like fossil fuels, are dwindling. The world's mightiest rivers – the Ganges, the Niger and the Yellow River – are drying up. The glaciers at the source of many of these great rivers are melting because of climate change: as they disappear so does the water. In a world of altered weather patterns, rainfall alone cannot refill the aquifers deep in the earth – and those that are replenished by rain are becoming polluted by fertilisers and pesticides from industrial farming, and by sewage and other chemicals that gradually seep into the groundwater. In many parts of both the developed and developing world meeting the daily water needs of an exploding population is increasingly difficult. With large companies buying up supplies around the world, it is no wonder that water is now being called 'blue gold'. As its scarcity grows, scientists and politicians believe that future wars will be fought over this 'new oil'.

Then there is the problem of an increasing population putting ever greater pressure on our dwindling natural resources. Currently the world population stands at 6.6 billion. By 2050 the figure is expected to rise to 9.1 billion. The challenge will not simply be producing enough food, but making sure that it reaches the people who need it, wherever they are in the world.

MAKING CHANGES

Clearly our current methods of food production aren't coping, and in fact were never designed to cope, with such pressures. The goals of today's food system — to intensify production and increase yields by any means, and to build a global marketplace for food — were defined more than 70 years ago in a very different world.

This system has focused too closely on food as a commodity — one that must continually grow in an economic sense. But if we keep producing, buying and eating food the way we do now our food horizons, and those of future generations, will narrow considerably.

It doesn't have to be like this. We need a modern food system that offers real, sustainable alternatives for feeding a growing population and remaining resilient in the face of peak oil and climate change. A system that engages with the world as it is today, not the world we lived in nearly a century ago.

This doesn't mean giving way to a techno-world where food is grown in test tubes or vast multi-storey laboratories, but moving forward with what works and leaving behind what doesn't.

This means new economies on a local scale that cut down the giants of industrialisation and globalisation to a more workable and productive, and less wasteful, size.

OR FOOD ARE AMONG THE PERFORM ON A DAILY BASIS.

Such an economy calls for us to embrace more fully the practice and principles of organic agriculture, which avoids the use of synthetic pesticides or fertilisers (as well as antibiotics, hormones, genetic engineering and radiation). Organic farming works with the land to minimise damage to the soil, to the environment and to wildlife, and, in some cases, it is far more productive per hectare than intensive farming. Sourced close to home, it is also fresher, less wasteful and more nutritious.

It doesn't matter whether we approach this 'food problem' from the perspective of a fresh-food enthusiast, a farmer looking to keep his farm productive and profitable, a politician addressing food security and population growth, a climate activist or a concerned parent thinking about their children's future. All roads lead to the same holy trinity: organic, local, seasonal.

That's what this book is about. It is a call to action that asks everyone to understand, envision and participate in making new choices and necessary changes. The solutions are out there in our kitchens, our gardens, our communities, on both the national and international level. Let's start making it happen by making food activism a part of everyday life.

You don't have to be out on the street waving a banner to be a food activist. You can show that you care about healthy, sustainable food in your own way and in your own home. If we continue to rely on the current system of food production we will all lose. We may even reach a point where changes we could once have made voluntarily are enforced from above. It is not unthinkable that there will be a time when rationing could come back into force. Why wait for this to happen? It is unnecessary and it would infantilise us instead of inspiring and empowering us to change.

We can all reconnect with food in a meaningful way. We can enjoy a diet full of variety in the knowledge that our food supply is healthy and secure. But we need to get going right now.

What we eat matters. In fact, growing, eating and shopping for food are among the most political acts any of us perform on a daily basis. The choices that we make in these actions are powerful and shape the world that we live in. We need, then, to start making choices that lead to a new food system that is productive and sustainable — one that goes by the mantra of 'good food for all', not, 'cheap food for all'.

If we don't, we really are stuffed.

01
IN THE KITCHEN

ORGANIC. LOCAL. SEASONAL.

EVERY FOOD CHOICE WE MAKE IS A STATEMENT ABOUT
WHO WE ARE AND HOW WE WANT TO LIVE. IT ALSO HAS
A POWERFUL INFLUENCE ON THE KIND OF WORLD WE WANT
IN THE FUTURE. SO WHY NOT START THE REVOLUTION NOW,
RIGHT IN YOUR OWN KITCHEN?

FEEDING OURSELVES

IT USED TO BE A SIMPLE TRANSACTION. WE GREW FOOD AND WE ATE IT.

AND IF WE DIDN'T GROW IT
PERSONALLY WE KNEW THE MAN
WHO DID BECAUSE HE LIVED
ONLY A SHORT DISTANCE AWAY.
TODAY THINGS ARE DIFFERENT.
IT STILL GETS GROWN AND
IT STILL GETS EATEN, BUT THE
STEPS IN BETWEEN HAVE
BECOME LONGER, AND MUCH
MORE COMPLICATED.

More often than not, we don't know where our food has come from. We don't know who grew it, how they grew it, how far it has travelled to get to us, who prepared it, or what has happened to it in the journey from farm to fork.

The more complicated things become, the more we look for shortcuts and symbols that help make them simple again. For instance, when you buy a potato from a farmer you are buying a potato. You take it home and boil, mash or fry it. It doesn't come with instructions. When you buy a potato pie, however, you need a label to tell you what it is, who made it, what's in it, how it should be cooked, what its use-by date is, and even sometimes 'serving suggestions' for what other foods you should eat with it.

The more disconnected we become from our food supply the more complex our food labels become. They tell us how much salt, sugar and fat are inside, how many calories it contains, and what proportion of our 'recommended daily intake' this forms. As concerns about waste and CO_2 emissions increase, labels also tell us what the package is made of, and how it can be recycled – or not. In some cases they even carry a carbon footprint indicator to tell us how much closer the food we are eating is taking the world towards climate catastrophe.

The globalised food system and the numerous ways it contributes to climate change, economic uncertainty, environmental degradation and the widespread decline in human health is complex. But when all is said and done the rules for eating sustainably, eating economically, and eating well can, if we want, be greatly simplified. This simplicity, in turn, is the key to a secure food supply.

This is a book about food activism, and the truth is that the revolution doesn't begin on the high street. It begins in our homes. It begins in our kitchens with the food we choose to eat, how we store and prepare it, how much we waste and how willing we are to try new ideas and learn new skills.

Sharpening our cooking skills, choosing food that is fresh, organic and in season in preference to highly processed food or ready meals, eating less meat and cooking in an energy efficient way may seem like small actions but in the context of climate change and peak oil they are also highly political choices and a practical, rational response to the problems facing the world. The more of us who choose to shop and cook and eat in this way, the greater the positive impact will be.

WITH A GROWING DEMAND FOR GENUINELY GOOD, CLEAN, FAIR, SUSTAINABLE FOOD, THE BENCHMARKS HAVE BEEN RAISED. THIS HAS BEEN MET WITH A PLETHORA OF LABELLING. INSTEAD OF ONE BOTTOM LINE WE NOW NEGOTIATE AT LEAST FOUR: IS IT HEALTHY? IS IT ORGANIC? IS IT FAIRLY TRADED? HOW FAR HAS IT TRAVELLED? AT TIMES EXERCISING INFORMED CHOICE CAN FEEL LIKE A FULL-TIME JOB.

More than anything else, this new interest in ethical shopping indicates a break away from a consumerism based solely on economic value to one based on social values rooted in less tangible, but equally important, concepts such as connection, community and care for others – especially those who live far away.

'Caring at a distance', as ethical shopping is sometimes defined, can help to support people in the developing world. But it can also produce high levels of pollution through air miles and manufacturing emissions, and mountains of waste through the multi-layered packaging required to move goods around the globe and store them on market shelves. It can also leave locally produced goods, services and communities in the UK without investment.

A telling piece of research at the Center for Agroecology and Sustainable Food Systems, University of California Santa Cruz in 2005 showed how easy it is to get shunted down a single avenue of 'caring' and lose sight of the bigger picture, even when you are trying to shop ethically. Researchers in California found that when asked to rank the importance of five eco labels (indicating whether a product was humanely reared, locally grown, provided a living wage to workers, US grown or from a small-scale producer) nearly twice as many people said they were concerned about animal welfare than those who were concerned about the welfare of those who grew and picked their food (30% versus 16%).

SHOPPING WITH A CONSCIENCE

Some labels are genuinely useful. When you buy an organic product, for instance, you are assured of sustainably produced foods without synthetic pesticides or fertilisers, antibiotics, hormones, genetic engineering or radiation. Organic farming minimises damage to the environment and wildlife. If it is home grown you are also getting fresh food, with a higher nutrient value.

But beware labels that hide from us as much information as they tell. Maybe more. They can hide the thousands of miles our food travels, the dozens of steps needed to procure and add the various ingredients, the working conditions of the people who grow and produce it, the levels of pesticide residues, the conditions the animals were kept in, the energy involved, the water used, the pollution emitted, the waste dumped.

The eco labels that we use as guides have become a kind of everyday ballot, and the choice of ethical goods a statement of intent for many people that says, 'these are the things I care about'. But to be effective, that caring needs to be accompanied by informed action.

DECODING THE LABEL

ORGANIC

As faith in the quality and safety of conventionally produced food declines, the popularity of organic food rises. There are six certification bodies in the UK. Of these, the oldest and largest is the Soil Association, certifying 80% of all organic produce in the UK. Its independent standards exceed the EU minimum organic standards. Of all the labels found on our food the organic label does more to guarantee that a product is healthy for people and for the planet.

What the label means

- Produced to a minimum EU organic standard
- Environmentally friendly
- No use of synthetic fertilisers
- Pesticides avoided
- Maintains soil fertility
- All animals are free range
- High animal welfare standards
- Antibiotics restricted
- No growth hormones
- No GM
- No irradiation
- Traceability
- Better for wildlife

What it doesn't mean

- Local
- Consistency in standards of certifying bodies
- Low air miles
- Sourced from small producers
- Minimal packaging

FAIRTRADE

Fair trade is a strategy for alleviating poverty by ensuring that producers receive a fair price for their goods, and support and education for sustainable farming practices. The fairtrade label can be found on food such as coffee and bananas to jeans, jewellery and flowers.

What the label means

- Producers get a fair price for their goods
- Extra income for farmers, artisans and agricultural workers
- Small farmers have access to world markets

What it doesn't mean

- Lower food miles
- Locally produced
- No animal cruelty
- Organic
- Minimal packaging
- Fair trade throughout the supply chain

CONSERVATION GRADE

A UK-based agricultural system that aims to increase wildlife species on farming land, without compromising farming sustainability. Under this scheme farmers must set aside 10% of their land to create habitats for wildflowers, birds, insects and small animals. This creates a more environmentally-friendly product, but it is not the same as organic.

What the label means

- Preserves natural habitats
- Fewer pesticides
- Produced in the UK

What it doesn't mean

- Organic
- Pesticide-free
- Minimal packaging

MARINE STEWARDSHIP COUNCIL

The Marine Stewardship Council (MSC) label promotes sustainable fisheries by: maintaining and re-establishing healthy populations of targeted species; maintaining the integrity of ecosystems; developing and maintaining effective management systems, taking into account all relevant biological, technological, economic, social, environmental and commercial aspects; and complying with relevant local, national and international laws, standards and agreements.

What the label means

- Sustainably managed fisheries
- Attempts to re-establish endangered species
- Best practice in catching fish
- Respect of the marine environment

What it doesn't mean

- Sustainable practices used after the fish are caught
- Farmed fish excluded

- Fish are never taken from depleted stocks
- Fair access to certification for small-scale fishermen

FREEDOM FOOD

The Freedom Food mark found on eggs, dairy, meat, poultry and salmon products means the animals have been reared, handled, transported and slaughtered to RSPCA standards. These include freedom from hunger and thirst, discomfort, pain, injury, disease, distress, and the freedom to express normal behaviour. It applies to indoor and outdoor farming methods but is aspirational rather than strict. Certification will not be withheld if these standards are not fully met.

What the label means

- Welfare standards may be above minimum
- No battery cages for hens

What it doesn't mean

- Free range animals/outdoor access
- High environmental standards on farms

- No mutilations (tail docking and beak trimming)
- Animals fed natural diets
- Organic

RED TRACTOR

This food industry certificate means that meat, vegetable, fruit, flour, sugar and dairy products have been produced to the minimum standards of welfare, environment and hygiene required by law. Use of the logo is granted by the Assured Food Standards, an agribusiness umbrella group representing the National Farmers Union, the Meat and Livestock Commission, Dairy UK and the British Retail Consortium. The British flag was added to the logo to denote products that have been 'produced, processed and packed in the UK'.

What the label means

- Food produced to a minimum UK/European standard

What it doesn't mean

- Not intensively reared

- Animals treated well, given outdoor access
- No mutilations
- No GM
- No growth promoters
- Locally/UK grown ingredients
- Organic

LEAF MARQUE

An industry funded certification scheme that encourages efficient farming systems and good farming practice. It covers areas such as soil management and crop nutrition, pesticide usage, pollution control, waste management, water and energy efficiency and the protection of wildlife and landscape.

What the label means

- A minimum standard for environmental care

What it doesn't mean

- Organic
- Small scale
- No GM
- Animals not intensively reared
- Locally/UK produced

WHAT IS HEALTHY FOOD?

- FOOD PRODUCED IN SEASON CLOSE TO WHERE YOU LIVE

- FOOD THAT IS GROWN IN A WAY THAT KEEPS THE SOIL HEALTHY

- FOOD GROWN WITHOUT THE AID OF ARTIFICIAL PESTICIDES OR FERTILISERS

- FOOD THAT COMES FROM ETHICALLY RAISED ANIMALS

- FOOD THAT ENSURES FARMERS ARE PAID THE REAL VALUE OF WHAT THEY PRODUCE

- FOOD THAT IS PRODUCED WITH ATTENTION TO WORKER WELFARE

- FOOD THAT DOESN'T EXPLOIT OUR NATURAL RESOURCES AND MAINTAINS THE DIVERSITY OF ECOSYSTEMS

AND THEN THERE WAS NONE...

THIS IS HOW MANY PLANETS WE HAVE.

THIS IS HOW MANY PLANETS IT WILL TAKE TO MAINTAIN OUR CURRENT FOOD SYSTEM.

HOW LONG CAN WE CONTINUE BEFORE OUR GLOBAL CUPBOARDS ARE BARE?

MOST OF US THINK THAT HEALTHY FOOD IS FOOD THAT IS GOOD FOR YOUR BODY.

But with the effects of peak oil and climate change pressing in on us, the definition of 'healthy food' needs to meet a new and all-encompassing criteria. Our choices at home will be an important driving force for reshaping this food culture. In addition to being low in salt, processed sugar, hydrogenated fat and additives, the real definition of healthy food must include the following points:

It should also include food that doesn't require the kind of hard sell that encourages us to make choices against all our desires for healthy eating.

If you make locally produced food a priority on your shopping list, you are also helping to support those whose skills we will need to rely on as climate change and the energy crisis take hold.

DON'T BUY ANY FOOD YOU'VE EVER SEEN ADVERTISED.

NINETY-FOUR PER CENT OF AD BUDGETS FOR FOOD GO TO PROCESSED FOOD...SO THE REAL FOOD IS NOT BEING ADVERTISED, AND THAT'S REALLY ALL YOU NEED TO KNOW.

MICHAEL POLLAN

CHANGING

1 It takes nearly 5000 litres of water to produce 1 kilogram of pork. This is the equivalent of taking a 16 hour shower.

2 To produce a tonne of pork takes six tonnes of carbon dioxide. This is the same amount of carbon dioxide produced by each household in the UK through their use of energy — enough to fill six hot air balloons 10 metres in diameter.

3 Livestock production in the Amazon alone currently accounts for nearly 14% of annual global deforestation.

4 In a world where nearly a billion people are starving, a third of all cereal crops and more than 90% of soya goes into animal feed, not food for humans.

5 It takes 22.2kg of soya beans to produce the amount of poultry meat eaten by an average citizen in the UK in a year. Millions of tonnes of carbon dioxide are being released in the atmosphere as tropical forests in South America are being destroyed to grow soya to feed chickens and pigs in Europe.

6 Cutting the average UK family's meat consumption in half would reduce household emissions more than cutting car use in half.

||||||||||||||||||||||||||||||||||||||||||||||||||||||||||||||||||||||||||||||||||||||||||||||||||||
IN THE DEVELOPED WORLD, WE CURRENTLY ENJOY
||||||||||||||||||||||||||||||||||||||||||||||||||||||||||||||||||||||||||||||||||||||||||||||||||||
A DIET THAT IS HIGH IN MEAT AND DAIRY, BUT THESE
||||||||||||||||||||||||||||||||||||||||||||||||||||||||||||||||||||||||||||||||||||||||||||||||||||
FOODS ARE AMONG THE MOST ENERGY INTENSIVE
||||||||||||||||||||||||||||||||||||||||||||||||||||||||||||||||||||||||||||||||||||||||||||||||||||
OF ALL THE FOODS WE EAT.
||||||||||||||||||||||||||||||||||||||||||||||||||||||||||||||||

Agriculture is a major contributor to global greenhouse gas (GHG) emissions, giving out around 30% of all GHGs emitted in the world. Livestock is responsible for the largest proportion of this — about 18% of global GHGs. That's more than the total emissions from transport.

This matters because in the UK and globally we need to make an 80% reduction in GHGs by 2050 if we are to have a chance of keeping below a 2°C rise in temperatures, above which runaway climate change becomes a real possibility.

Not all systems of producing meat are the same. For example, grass reared, sustainably produced livestock plays a role in storing carbon in the soil, which may go a long way to offsetting the methane emissions from grass-fed cattle and sheep.

Meat and dairy products currently make up a third of humanity's protein intake, and demand is growing fast. In 2000, global meat consumption was 230 million tonnes per year. Estimates suggest that the livestock industry is aiming to double its production by 2050 in order to feed a rising population, all of whom, it is assumed, will be consuming the same meat-heavy diet that the developed world currently eats. A large proportion of this increase will be intensively produced white meat.

THE MENU

This is not possible, nor is it healthy for the planet or its people. In fact, the healthiest populations are those who mainly eat a plant-based diet. This is not the same as a vegetarian diet, which eschews all meat (and sometimes dairy). A plant-based diet is made up mostly of plant foods – fruits, vegetables, grains and pulses – and includes grass-reared, sustainably produced meat in about half the quantities that we comsume today.

So we do not need to stop eating meat altogether. Meat provides high quality protein and eating a small amount is healthy. But the bottom line is that the era of cheap meat is over. In the future we need to eat meat that is sustainable and produced to a higher ethical standard – one that takes into account the needs of the animals, the consumer and the planet. This means a return to grazing livestock that is organically, rather than intensively, raised.

A low-meat diet is also the best use of land. In 2007 researchers at Cornell University compared 42 different diets that contained the same number of calories and a core of locally produced grain, fruit, vegetable and dairy products and varying amounts of meat.

They found that a low-meat diet, as opposed to a strict vegetarian diet, was actually the most land-efficient, and therefore most climate-friendly. Fruits, vegetables and grains require high quality cropland, while meat can be produced on lower quality, more widely available, pastureland. Grazing livestock in this way, instead of turning it over to crop production, also ensures that carbon locked in the soil stays there. For more on efficient land use, see Chapter 6.

MYTHS OF A LIFE WITHOUT MEAT

1 We need cow's milk for calcium
More than 20 plant-based foods contain more calcium than milk, including dark green vegetables, dried fruits, nuts, seeds and pulses.

2 Without meat we lack iron
A balanced plant-based diet provides easily as much iron as meat. Good sources are pulses, green vegetables, wholegrains and dark chocolate.

3 A vegan diet lacks protein
A balanced vegan diet has all the protein you need – from soya products, quinoa, pulses, nuts and wholegrain foods.

4 Oily fish boosts brain power
Fish oils are not essential for cognitive ability. Plant-based omega-3 fats (e.g. from flaxseed and rapeseed) are a healthier, more sustainable alternative.

5 Chicken is the healthy option
Chicken is not in fact lower in fat than red meat. Because of intensive farming their flesh now contains twice as much fat as in 1940.

6 Soya is bad for you
There is a vigorous 'anti soya' crusade about soya phytoestrogens (plant hormones). But there is no evidence that soya foods harm human health.

Dr Justine Butler (Senior Health Campaigner at the Vegetarian and Vegan Foundation and Viva) and Dale Vince (founder of Ecotricity and owner of the Zerocarbonista blog).

THE HIDDEN ENVIRONMENTAL COSTS OF SUGAR AND SALT

SUGARCANE CAUSES

- biodiversity loss in tropical countries through destruction of habitat to make way for large plantations

- intensive use of water for irrigation

- the heavy use of agricultural chemicals

- water pollution — run-off from the sugar industry in Australia, for example, is partly responsible for the destruction of the Great Barrier Reef

- sugar beet cultivation can contaminate surrounding land through water pollution and carries the added danger of genetic modification if grown in the US

SALT CAUSES

- Large salt producing enterprises can have a negative impact on fragile marine environments such as mangroves

FACT:
It only takes 120 extra calories per day to gain a pound of extra weight per month.

RECENT DECADES HAVE SEEN THE WORLD SUFFERING FROM 'PORTION DISTORTION' AS 'NORMAL' PORTION SIZES HAVE CREPT UP.

This is particularly true in fast food restaurants, which compete to supersize their meals and provide value for money. Supermarkets also encourage the trend for more food with larger size packages and incentives such as 'three for the price of two'. Excess food on our plates and bigger package sizes have increased the amount we eat by 43% in the last few decades.

Switching to a climate-friendly diet of sensible servings is not only better for our health but better for the planet too. High rates of obesity in richer countries leads to a higher demand for food and therefore more transport emissions, releasing extra tonnes of GHGs each year.

THINK SMALLER

Reducing portion size isn't about going hungry – it's about returning a sensible balance to our diets. One of the reasons we overeat is that highly processed foods fail to give our bodies what they need nutritionally, so we buy more, we eat more (and we also waste more). A diet of fresh food is not only more filling per serving, it is more nutritious and better for the environment too.

	1950S	TODAY
HAMBURGER (WITH BUN)	110g	125–357g
HAMBURGER (NO BUN)	45g	up to 227g
FRENCH FRIES	68g	up to 201g
SOFT DRINKS	198g	340g–1.8kg
PASTA (SINGLE SERVING)	210g	420g
MUFFIN	85g	184g
CHOCOLATE BAR	28g	74–227g

THEN AND NOW

IN 50 YEARS PORTION SIZES HAVE INCREASED DRAMATICALLY, MIRRORED BY A RISE IN OBESITY IN RICHER COUNTRIES.

LEARNING NEW SKILLS

WE LIVE IN A WORLD WHERE MANY OF US HAVE BECOME DESKILLED. LIFE SKILLS THAT WERE ONCE PASSED ON FROM PARENT TO CHILD HAVE GIVEN WAY TO A WORLD OF SERVICE INDUSTRIES WHERE WE PAY SOMEONE ELSE TO DO THINGS FOR US. THIS IS PARTICULARLY TRUE WITH FOOD PREPARATION.

The UK currently consumes more ready meals than any other European country (46% of those sold). When we're not eating ready meals we are eating on the go; we are also Europe's biggest consumers of fast food, and burgers are our favourite food on the go. Those of us who think eating fresh, local, seasonal, organic food is too expensive, take note: government figures show that we spend £7.6 billion – a quarter of our total eating-out spend – on fast food, including fish and chips, pizza, burgers and Thai, Chinese and Indian takeaways.

In a ready meal culture many of us have disconnected from and become deskilled in the art and science of cooking and storing food. Schools no longer teach these skills as a matter of routine (though this is beginning to change, see Chapter 4) and as a result several generations of adults no longer understand the basics of feeding themselves.

How to change? All over the country courses are available to help people acquire skills such as how to choose fresh and seasonal produce, how to store it and cook it, for themselves. Our children are keen to learn and many older members of our communities have tremendous knowledge to share when it comes to kitchen table know-how. Let's get them together. Making use of these resources to become self-sufficient in our own kitchens could be one of the most radical investments we make in the future.

ENERGY EFFICIENT COOKING

Around 2% of our home energy goes into cooking, while another 3% powers our fridges and freezers – more than double the energy we use to power televisions and computers and to light our homes. There are many ways to cook in a more energy efficient way. Here's one to try:

|||||||||||||||||||||||||||||||||||||||||||||||||
HOT-BOX COOKING
|||||||||||||||||||||||||||||||||||||||||||||||||

A hot box is a no-energy way of cooking rice, pulses, soups and stews – anything that can be left all day and improve with slow cooking. It works on the same principle as slow cookers, or crock pots. It is a large, super-insulated box that holds a single cooking pot. It can be as simple as one cardboard box inside another with several inches of insulating material in between, or as complex as a specially constructed wooden box or drawer in your kitchen. The key to success is not what it looks like on the outside, but how well you insulate it. Straw is the traditional material but you can also use foam board, cushions filled with polystyrene beads or polyester wadding, or even old newspapers and wool.

Ingredients for your meal are heated briefly on the stove, or mixed with boiling water, and then left to cook in a well-insulated environment. Food stays hot for up to eight hours, reaching approximately 56°C, and remains warm for a few hours more. Nothing burns and everything cooks to perfection. Why not give it a try?

SPRING

ASPARAGUS BROAD BEANS CAULIFLOWER CHICORY DUCK EARLY CARROTS FORCED RHUBARB GARLIC GREEN CABBAGE KALE LEMON SOLE LETTUCE LOBSTER NETTLES RADISHES ROCKET SARDINES SEA TROUT SCALLOPS SPINACH SORREL SPRING CHICKEN SPRING GREENS SPRING LAMB SPROUTING BROCCOLI

SUMMER

BEETROOT BLACKCURRANTS BROCCOLI CHERRIES COD COURGETTES CRAB CUCUMBER ENGLISH VEAL FENNEL FRENCH BEANS GOOSEBERRIES HARE LETTUCE LOGANBERRIES NEW POTATO ONIONS OUTDOOR RHUBARB PEAS PILCHARDS PLUMS RASPBERRIES REDCURRANT STRING BEANS STRAWBERRIE SWEET CORN TARRAGON TOMATOES WELSH LAMB

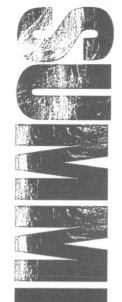

WINTER

BEETROOT BROCCOLI BRUSSELS SPROUTS CARROTS CAULIFLOWER CELERIAC CELERY CHICORY GOOSE HADDOCK HALIBUT HERRING KALE LEEKS LOBSTER MACKEREL MUSSELS PARSNIPS RED CABBAGE SAVOY CABBAGE SCALLOPS SEA BASS SHALLOTS SPINACH SPROUTING BROCCOLI SQUASH SWEDE TURKEY

AUTUMN

APPLES BLACKBERRIES BROCCOLI BROWN TROUT CABBAGE CARROTS CAULIFLOWER CELERIAC CHESTNUTS CUCUMBER DAMSONS DUCK FENNEL FRENCH BEANS GOOSE GROUSE HADDOCK LEEKS LETTUCE MUSSELS OYSTERS PARSNIPS PARTRIDGE PEARS PLUMS POTATOES PUMPKIN RUNNER BEANS SEA BASS VENISON

LIVING WITHIN OUR LIMITS

FACT:
Food transport now accounts for 1.8% of the total annual CO_2 emissions in the UK and 8.7% of the total emissions from UK road use.

AS CLIMATE CHANGE AND RESOURCE DEPLETION BITE, YOU MAY WONDER WHAT THE FUTURE HOLDS AND HOW WELL EQUIPPED YOU ARE TO MEET THE CHALLENGES AHEAD. WHILE WE HAVE BECOME USED TO LIVING – AND EATING – WITHOUT LIMITS, A DIET FOR A HEALTHY WORLD WILL NECESSARILY MEAN UNDERSTANDING CURRENT AND FUTURE LIMITATIONS OF OUR FOOD SUPPLY AND MAKING CHANGES.

Certain types of foods, such as exotic products from far away and highly processed foods, will make up much less of our diet than they do now, giving way instead to fresh, local and seasonal foods, as well as more dried and preserved staples.

Long supply chains make exotic foods more vulnerable to price rises if supplies or crops fail. The distance our food travels means that fresh produce loses its nutritional value in transit, may be treated with fungicides and pesticides, or have added preservatives to prolong its life. Each of these increases the carbon footprint of a meal. This is an inefficient, unsustainable and unhealthy way to eat.

Locally based food systems are more resilient. They have shorter and therefore more secure supply chains. This food tends to be cheaper and fresher, and retain more nutrients.

Sourcing locally, whether from a box scheme or a farmers' market gives you a chance to experiment with varieties, from colourful heritage tomatoes to rare breeds of beef. Because the food goes more or less directly from farm to fork there are fewer hidden road and air miles and less need for refrigeration en route.

If you are tempted by chilled ready meals for convenience, remember they often require many different ingredients from multiple global destinations, all of which increases their carbon footprint. Storing them requires energy during shipment, at the supermarket and at home. It is true that electrical appliances are becoming more energy efficient, but, still, the energy needed to ship, store and cook food is running out.

Salad vegetables in the middle of winter may become a thing of the past. By devoting a cupboard in your kitchen instead to dried, canned and preserved staples you can lower food waste and the energy used in food storage.

Likewise, eating seasonally is a meaningful way to go about a low-impact lifestyle, while shopping locally will give you a more realistic sense of what's available at different times of year.

WASTE NOT WANT NOT

OUR COMPLICITY WITH, AND ARROGANCE ABOUT, FOOD WASTE MUST END NOW. DID YOU KNOW WE THROW AWAY AROUND 25% OF ALL FOOD WE BUY IN THE UK? THAT WORKS OUT AT £680 PER YEAR FOR THE AVERAGE UK HOUSEHOLD WITH CHILDREN. ALONG THE FOOD SUPPLY CHAIN ANOTHER 25% USED TO BE THROWN AWAY ROUTINELY BECAUSE IT DIDN'T MEET AESTHETIC STANDARDS. ONLY IN 2009, EU LEGISLATION PREVENTING THE SALE OF 'UGLY' PRODUCE WAS FINALLY SCRAPPED.

It is no longer illegal to sell misshapen or oddly sized apricots, artichokes, asparagus, aubergines, avocados, beans, Brussels sprouts, carrots, cauliflowers, cherries, courgettes, cucumbers, cultivated mushrooms, garlic, hazelnuts in shells, headed cabbage, leeks, melons, onions, peas, plums, ribbed celery, spinach, walnuts in shells, watermelons and chicory. Even better, this produce is often up to 40% cheaper than its perfect counterparts.

Unfortunately for another 10 types of produce – apples, citrus fruit, kiwifruit, lettuces, peaches and nectarines, pears, strawberries, sweet peppers, grapes and tomatoes – which account for 75% of the EU fruit and vegetable trade, the rules, and the waste, remain unchanged.

Figures that say we need to double our food production by 2050 consistently fail to address the issue of food waste. In fact, there is enough food to feed everyone in the world right now. The problem is that the system of distribution ensures that only those who have enough money to play on the international market can come to the table.

You can address the issue of waste right now at home. By buying only what you need instead of whatever you want, you automatically buy less and therefore seamlessly reduce your impact in terms of pollution and waste.

MAKE A LIST

Check what's in your cupboards and your fridge and shop only for the extras you need. Planning what you want to buy and sticking to that plan reduces your 'foodprint', and can cut 20–25% off your weekly food bill. Don't be tempted to buy two for one offers unless you can genuinely use them. Look out for 'money off' promotions instead.

USE IT UP

Fruit that is going soft is still good for smoothies, pies and compotes. Vegetables that are a little past their best can be made into soups and veggie burgers.

LOVE YOUR LEFTOVERS

Instead of scraping leftovers into the bin, why not use them for tomorrow's meals? Leftover chicken can be added to a pasta bake, roast potatoes can make a salad for a light lunch, rice can be turned into a rice salad, and bits of bread can be used for breadcrumbs or bread-and-butter pudding. Use your imagination.

OLDEST FIRST

Reduce the risk of finding something mouldy and unidentifiable in your fridge by bringing any older items to the front when you bring new food home from the store.

FREEZE IT

If you have the freezer space you can freeze out-of-season soft fruits for later use, and cook meals in batches for reheating on evenings when you don't feel like cooking from scratch.

FEED THE GARDEN

Some food waste is unavoidable, so why not help feed the soil in your garden as well by starting a compost heap (see page 58–59).

THINGS YOU CAN MAKE THAT YOU THOUGHT YOU HAD TO BUY

TOMATO SAUCE	BREAD
YOGHURT	PICKLES / CHUTNEYS
JAM	DRIED HERBS
SOUP	BISCUITS
SALAD DRESSING	ORANGE JUICE

THERE ARE SO MANY FOOD PRODUCTS WE BUY THAT CAN EASILY BE MADE AT HOME. PREPARING THEM IN YOUR OWN KITCHEN MEANS YOU CAN MAKE AS LITTLE OR AS MUCH AS YOU NEED, AND YOU KNOW EVERY INGREDIENT THAT'S GONE IN AND WHERE IT HAS COME FROM. TRY IT OUT.

CALL TO ACTION

ACT NOW

- Have your local organic food delivered to your door.

- Challenge yourself to eat a 100 mile diet – where most of your food is produced within 100 miles of your home, leaving room for luxuries like coffee, tea, chocolate and spices!

- Leftovers account for a third of all food waste. Don't throw them away – turn them into a new meal instead.

- Put the lid on the pot – you'll save up to 6% of the energy used to cook with the lid off.

ACT TOGETHER

- Get together with your neighbours and buy in bulk from food cooperatives. This is a great, and affordable, way to stock up on staples such as dried and preserved goods, as well as more exotic items that have been sourced responsibly.

- Get your children involved in choosing and preparing meals.

- Start a community compost heap where neighbours can recycle food waste and in return receive great compost for their gardens.

ACT DIFFERENTLY

- Plan your weekly menus in advance and write a shopping list.

- Eat less meat and dairy. Choose grass-fed beef and lamb rather than intensively produced chicken or pork. Try going meat-free for one day a week.

- Take a break from ready-made meals. Start cooking again, and if you've never cooked before enrol in a class to learn.

- A healthy diet is based on variety. Try to eat something new each week and change your diet with the seasons.

- Take a foraging course and learn to identify food that grows in the wild. It's a good practical way of reconnecting yourself with nature.

DETERMINING HOW FAR YOUR FOOD HAS TRAVELLED IS ALMOST IMPOSSIBLE IN THE SUPERMARKET. THERE IS NO LABELLING SYSTEM TO HELP AND IF YOU BUY READY MEALS THEY MAY CONTAIN SO MANY INGREDIENTS SOURCED FROM SO MANY PLACES THAT EVEN THE MANUFACTURER COULDN'T TELL YOU HOW FAR THEY'VE ALL COME.

If you are concerned about climate change, consider the merits of a '100-mile diet', first advocated by Canadians Alisa Smith and J.B. MacKinnon. Instead of petty calorie-counting, this new way of eating counts food miles, and aims to make the majority of your diet come from within a 100-mile radius of your home.

It's a simple, positive action anyone can take to combat climate change; a way of thinking global and acting local. Eating this way could increase your intake of local foods from 15% to more than 80% of your total diet. It can also effortlessly change the profile of your diet to include higher levels of fruits, vegetables and grains, and lower levels of meat and dairy — all good for your health and without a single Lycra-clad diet 'expert' in sight.

If you live in the UK, going local, seasonal and organic is easy. Around 70% of organic food sold in this country is grown here so simply joining in with a local organic box scheme can boost the amount of UK-produced food in your diet. Shopping at a farmers' market means you are automatically buying produce that meets the requirements of the 100-mile diet: regulations set down by FARMA (the National Farmers' Retail and Markets Association) state that farms must be located within 30 miles (or 100 miles for London) to sell their produce at the local farmers' market.

Get yourself a map, draw a 100-mile radius from your home and research what you can get where. You will be surprised just how easy it is to feed yourself and your family well.

TIP: On market stalls or where loose organic produce is sold the seller should display a certificate from the accrediting body, and a trading schedule that lists which products on the stall are certified organic.

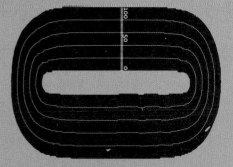

MILE DIET

Founder and Managing Director of the Duke of Cambridge
– the only Soil Association-certified pub in the UK

LOVE YOUR LEFTOVERS

HERE'S A RECIPE TO TACKLE THE FOOD WASTE CRISIS WE'RE IN. OPEN YOUR FRIDGE AND STORE CUPBOARD AND COOK UP A MEAL WITH WHATEVER'S IN THERE. SOUP MAYBE, BUBBLE AND SQUEAK, A PASTA DISH OR A RISOTTO. SIMPLE, ISN'T IT?

Unfortunately, the sad truth is that we throw away a quarter of the food we buy for our households — 8.3 million tonnes of it each year, equivalent to £680 of food for the average family of four. We throw out about 7% of the milk we buy, 36% of the bakery goods and more than 50% of the lettuce and leafy salads.

In the past, this waste all went to landfill, where it released noxious greenhouse gases. There are now many front-door food waste collections in the UK, turning the waste into compost. This is good news, but it's still all waste. Such schemes relieve us of some of our responsibility and guilt, but most of us ignore the energy required to process them.

Instead, we should be rethinking our approach to food. Visiting a supermarket without a clear meal plan inevitably leads to buying unnecessary ingredients. Enticed by 'two-for-one' bargains or tempted by heavily packaged delights, we come home and fill our storage space with unwanted food, which we then throw away. Bringing about change in our kitchens has to be tied to the way we shop and cook.

Time and money is often cited as the reason we cannot escape supermarkets. But shopping seasonally from street markets and small shops can save both time and money. You are less likely to buy ingredients and indulgences that you don't need, and popping to the local shops can be fast and more worthwhile. The money you spend is more likely to go into the local economy, you have a chance of meeting your neighbours, you will be contributing to the atmosphere of your high street, you are more likely to combine it into an existing journey, and you will use less packaging – grocery packaging from supermarkets makes up roughly a quarter of household waste.

The question, though, is how to plan a varied diet using up all our ingredients if we're no good at cooking? Some of the most appetising and yummy meals come from leftovers – a chicken carcass for stock or soup, the remains of the rocket to wilt in a pasta, odds and sods of cheese in a quiche or soufflé, all the roast trimmings for bubble and squeak, rice for a salad. The knowledge of how to use up leftovers has been lost over the past 40 years. We need urgently to regain this knowledge and immerse ourselves in the joys of small fridges and raw ingredients.

First, you need a good stock of store-cupboard staples – dried herbs, spices, pulses, condiments and tins – along with some imagination. Then you need some pre-planning: buying fresh food for just a day or two, eating in rotation from the fridge, using up first what will perish fastest. Or try buying nothing for a week and see what you can make from the existing supplies in your cupboards, fridge and freezer. Not only is this inspiring and fun, it could have a real impact on our environment. If we all stopped wasting food that could have been eaten, the reduction in our carbon footprint would be equivalent to taking one in four cars off the road.

It's not just in the home we have to make changes. The food service industry needs to rethink its approach to food entirely. At my pub, we change our menus daily so that today's over-preparing and mistakes can be amalgamated into tomorrow's treats. Think surplus mash into fishcakes; leftover bread into croutons or bread-and-butter pudding; a sponge cake burnt at the edges trimmed and reincarnated as a trifle. Working with a set menu never allows for the variables of running a kitchen, let alone cooking with local, seasonal ingredients.

Taking on the packaging of the catering trade is another whole ball game. This requires perseverance, time and energy. We send boxes back to some suppliers for reuse, which means more time and space needed for weekly collections. Suppliers are encouraged to avoid the use of heavy packaging – in fact, openly choosing suppliers on this basis is hugely effective.

Catering is not the only food waste criminal. The 'food grading' system in supermarkets rejects an enormous amount of food, while roughly 10% of the total world's fish catch is discarded – either because it is caught by accident or it is over the quota. This is particularly shocking and depressing when 70%–80% of the world's fish stocks are fully exploited, over-exploited, depleted or in recovery.

As the predicted population of the planet grows to nine billion by 2050, we will supposedly need to double food production. In fact, we need to double food 'availability' and use what we already have more efficiently. If we start to eat the one third of food we are currently throwing away, we could provide for millions more people.

Ultimately, food is a joyous part of our society. Growing food, cooking food, sharing meals together, even shopping for it in the right circumstances enhances our lives. These are not bourgeois pastimes – they are the fundamentals of our society. Husbandry, farming, harvesting, preserving, smoking, pickling and baking make up the history of our villages and towns from peasants to gentry. In the past, every crumb from the kitchen was consumed: pigs and chickens, for example, were fattened up on scraps, slaughtered for Christmas, then salted, smoked and hung to be used over the rest of the year. The motives for this kind of relationship with food may have been poverty or lack of availability, but lessons from this way of life must not be lost. Using the whole beast, the whole harvest, and the whole of the contents of our fridge must be our future and it will be a delicious one!

> *"If we all stopped wasting food, the reduction in our carbon footprint would be equivalent to taking one in four cars off the road."*

02

IN THE GARDEN

FOOD DOESN'T ALWAYS HAVE TO COME FROM ELSEWHERE. WHETHER YOU HAVE A TINY WINDOWSILL OR A LARGE GARDEN, GROWING YOUR OWN CAN HELP BRING GREATER VARIETY TO YOUR DIET, LOWER YOUR FOOD BILLS – AND YOUR CARBON FOOTPRINT – AND EMPOWER THE WHOLE FAMILY TO BECOME MORE SELF-SUFFICIENT.

FOOD PLOTS

IN 2009 VEGETABLE PATCHES
WERE PLANTED IN BOTH
10 DOWNING STREET AND
THE WHITE HOUSE.

When First Lady Michelle Obama began digging her organic garden she was making an important symbolic statement about self-sufficiency and the need for people to get back to the land. The converting of the Prime Minister's vegetable plot in Downing Street to organic echoed these sentiments, and helped raise the profile of the importance of organic food for the health of both people and the land. It also put our day-to-day relationship with food firmly back on the political menu, focusing attention on the huge energy inputs, and CO_2 outputs, of intensive agriculture and the increasing inability of the globalised food system to deliver food to everyone who needs it. Although the question was not explicitly voiced, it hung in the air: 'Does our food always have to come from somewhere else, and from someone else?'

The answer is a resounding 'no'. It can come right from your own back garden, windowsill, allotment or community vegetable patch.

Our gardens can be places of beauty and leisure. They can soothe tired eyes and nurture the soul, but all too often they fail to nourish the body as well. This is partly to do with the urbanisation of society and our disconnection from land as anything other than a pretty backdrop to our lives. It is also the result of a change in our food-gathering habits. As food has become so plentiful and easy to obtain outside our homes, we've lost the habit of using gardens to help feed our families.

But the interest in 'working gardens' has become greater as the economic crisis has deepened and the reality of peak oil draws closer. People are gradually realising that growing some of their own food is not only personally satisfying but crucial in a world where fossil fuels necessary to ship food across the globe can no longer be taken for granted. While a pretty garden has come to represent an ornamental add-on that increases a property's value, in future hard-working gardens that can put food on our tables may turn out to be much more valuable.

DOES OUR FOOD ALWAYS HAVE TO COME FROM SOMEWHERE ELSE, AND FROM SOMEONE ELSE?

THE ANSWER IS A RESOUNDING

NO

IT CAN COME RIGHT FROM YOUR OWN BACK GARDEN, WINDOWSILL, ALLOTMENT OR COMMUNITY VEGETABLE PATCH.

A PIZZA GARDEN

Gardens are important for children too. Just as they learn about human relations through the microcosm of the family, they learn about our human connection to the natural world through gardens and green spaces. Involving the whole family in the process of growing organic food is a way to teach our children that food does not come from shops, it comes from the soil and the sun. Creating and caring for your own little patch of garden is also a way of helping them understand why caring for planet Earth is so important. It also encourages them to eat the fruits of their labour, which, in turn, will promote healthy eating patterns for life.

Most children start their gardening experiments with fast-growing foods like parsley and sprouting seeds – from cress to mung beans to sunflower – which require very little space. Pumpkins, courgettes and other kinds of squash are also low maintenance and produce big results over time.

But if you want to try something more ambitious why not encourage your kids to grow a pizza garden. Herbs such as oregano and basil, and chives, garlic, even tomatoes smell great while they're growing and can be planted on sunny balconies or in containers. Use the harvest to make your own fresh toppings for a home-made pizza.

GROW ORGANIC

FACT:
A standard allotment can yield around a tonne of vegetables. If you bought the same amount of organic potatoes, onions, carrots and parsnips in a year, it would cost you around £300.

THERE ARE MANY GOOD REASONS WHY MORE OF US SHOULD WANT TO GROW OUR OWN FOOD.

There is a deep dissatisfaction with industrially grown produce, and a growing desire to nurture ourselves with fresh, nutrient-packed, organic food. There is an increased awareness of the links between food production, environmental degradation and energy depletion, and there is a growing political desire to resist the corporate takeover of agriculture. Many of us are tired of being beholden to large supermarkets and unwilling to contribute to the inequalities of the global free-trade system.

To grow your own food is to be empowered in a way that many of us have never experienced. It means less reliance on others. It takes pressure off our weekly food budgets. It also reconnects us with nature and soil and the seasons. And best of all, it can be great fun.

Growing your own food also gives you choice – to try new varieties and perhaps even preserve species that are in danger of dying out. Although supermarket shelves seem to be full of colour and variety, the truth is they stock a very narrow range of produce, which is bred for high yields and for successful shipment and storage rather than flavour.

But in your own garden you are in charge of what you grow. You can experiment with a range of fruit and vegetables full of flavour and colour; you can learn to save and swap seeds, and actively take part in preserving local food diversity. Every gardener who grows varieties that reflect local geography and food culture becomes, in effect, a resource for future biodiversity.

Every garden is connected to the larger landscape in ways that most of us could never imagine. Gardens provide green corridors for birds and bees, helping to boost the populations of these vital pollinators and seed dispersers. Putting a small pond in your garden will attract and provide habitat for birds, insects and frogs, all good for pest control as well as for maintaining diversity.

Whatever the reasons for having an organic garden at home the outcome is a win-win situation – it decreases energy consumption and economic vulnerability, it puts nourishing, tasty food on the table that improves the family's physical and mental health, and it also increases local biodiversity and environmental stability.

THERE WAS A TIME WHEN THE KNOWLEDGE OF HOW TO GROW YOUR OWN FOOD WAS A PART OF OUR CULTURAL LITERACY. IT CAN BE AGAIN. WHETHER YOU HAVE A BIG GARDEN, A SMALL ONE OR ONLY A FEW TUBS OR WINDOW BOXES YOU CAN GROW FOOD FOR YOUR OWN TABLE.

Many of us are already doing this as we become more concerned about food shortages and higher prices in the supermarkets. Around a third of Britons currently grow some of their own food and surveys show that many more of us would like to, but lack the confidence to get started.

A 2008 survey by the Soil Association found that a massive 92% of us think self-sufficiency is important, especially during the economic downturn. However, almost half (47%) feel less able to grow our own food than previous generations did. A similar number have fewer cooking skills than our grandparents and 51% of us have no idea how to rear animals.

The knowledge hasn't been entirely lost, just misplaced, and reacquiring it is not such a difficult journey. You don't need to go to elaborate lengths or invest in masses of new equipment. Think of what you like to eat, find a spot in your garden or on your windowsill, and have a go. Most people find that once they harvest something they've grown themselves, they become hooked. They read more, grow more, acquire more skills and knowledge, and before they know it they've put themselves on a path to becoming more self-sufficient.

Something else changes as well. You become more connected to your neighbourhood and community. If one neighbour is growing leeks and the other potatoes, a trade in excess springs up and spreads the bounty around. This alternative

economy forges a different awareness of, and a more direct bond with, the people around you. It soon becomes apparent that putting down roots in your own garden eventually taps you into a different kind of community spirit (see Chapter 3), which becomes a welcome bridge in a time of cultural transition to life without oil.

WANT TO LEARN MORE?

One way to learn skills and connect with your community is to join a local gardening club. Many neighbourhoods have them and you can usually find them through your local newspaper, community centre or garden centre. The Soil Association also has local groups around the country that are actively involved in gardening.

Alternatively, the Soil Association's Organic Farm School, supported by the Daylesford Foundation, has more than 300 hands-on courses in growing your own food, rearing animals, cooking and rural crafts. Whether you are trying to make your life more sustainable, learn to live closer to the land, or find inspiration for a possible new career, these courses give you a great opportunity to acquire a whole range of new and useful skills. See **www.soilassociation.org/ farmschool.aspx.**

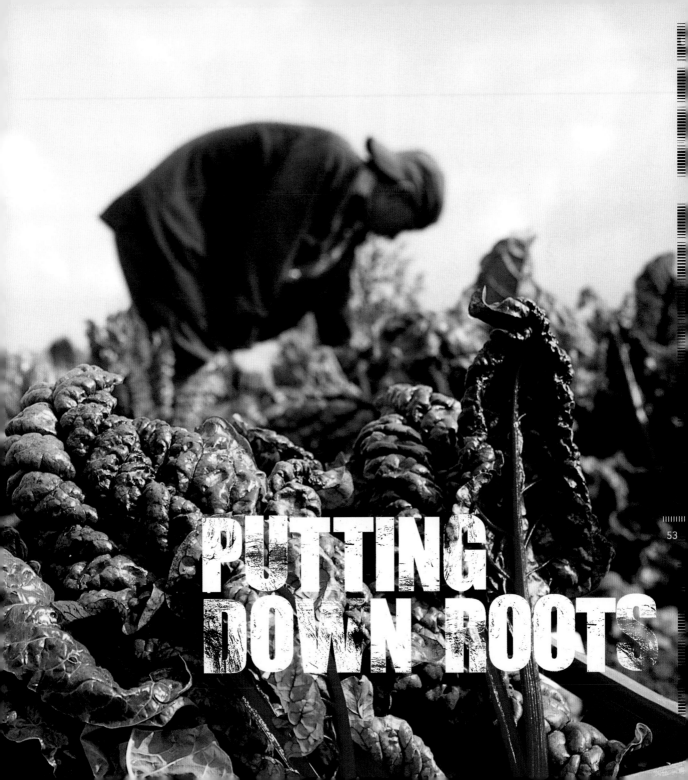

PUTTING
DOWN ROOTS

SEEDING DIVERSITY

FACT:
Garden Organic's Adopt-a-Veg makes a great ethical gift to help to secure the future of rare heritage vegetables. www.gardenorganic.org.uk

WHEN THE UK JOINED THE EUROPEAN COMMUNITY (EC) IN 1973 IT WAS REQUIRED TO CREATE A LIST OF OFFICIALLY 'APPROVED' SEED VARIETIES. THIS WAS INTENDED TO ENSURE THAT ALL SEEDS SOLD IN THE EC WERE OF GOOD QUALITY. BUT GETTING YOUR SEEDS ON THE SEED LIST COSTS THOUSANDS OF POUNDS EACH YEAR, WHICH MEANT THAT ONLY LARGE COMPANIES COULD ENSURE THEIR VARIETIES WERE LISTED. AS A RESULT, THE UK AND EUROPE HAVE LOST THOUSANDS OF VARIETIES OF FRUITS AND VEGETABLES.

This scenario is being repeated all over the world, and is being made worse by large agribusinesses patenting seed varieties to restrict their use (see Chapter 7).

This is a tragedy because genetic diversity is what keeps a food supply strong. Many older, locally appropriate varieties of produce are resistant to local pests, diseases and extremes of weather. This makes them perfect for an organic garden.

To sell seeds not on the approved list is illegal, but many gardeners get round this by organising informal seed swaps. As no money changes hands this is not illegal. You can also gain access to heritage seeds by becoming a member of the Heritage Seed Library, which safeguards around 800 rare vegetable varieties. Many of its seeds come from the 'Seed Guardians' – members who have volunteered to help produce seeds for the library. Of the 40,000 packets of seed sent out each year, nearly half are supplied by these Guardians devoted to safeguarding rare varieties.

To find out more about the different seeds available, or to join the Heritage Seed Library log on to **www.gardenorganic.org.uk/hsl**

SOIL SUPERST

BECOMING MORE AWARE OF YOUR GARDEN MEANS BECOMING MORE AWARE OF THE IMPORTANCE OF SOIL, BOTH ITS STRUCTURE AND ITS COMPOSITION. THROUGHOUT THE WORLD SOIL IS LOSING ITS ESSENTIAL NUTRIENTS AND AS A RESULT OUR FOOD IS BECOMING LESS NUTRITIOUS. THE SOIL IN OUR GARDENS IS NO EXCEPTION.

Your garden will contain the kind of soil that naturally occurs where you live combined with anything the previous owners have added to improve it. It will have a structure ranging from solid, airless clumps or loose, delicate particles interspersed with air and water. Many things can affect soil structure including how much water you apply, how much pressure you put on it, how often it is tilled, how much it is exposed to cold, rain and sun, and even what is being grown in it.

But the key to improving the structure of any soil is the addition of organic matter, ideally from your own compost heap.

RUCTURE

Soil is a living thing. Just a teaspoonful of healthy soil contains more than five billion living organisms, representing 10,000 or so different species. Soil that is healthy and cared for is teeming with microscopic life. These organisms are constantly breaking down plant and animal wastes and through this rebuilding nutrients. In the process they make minerals available to plants, helping them to grow and protecting them against toxins and disease. Without the activity of soil organisms – from microscopic bacteria to earthworms – life on the planet would cease. Chemical farming destroys these living communities, subjecting them to a non-stop toxic barrage of chemical fertilisers, herbicides, fungicides and insecticides, wiping out some species, encouraging others and disrupting the delicate balance below ground that helps plant life to thrive.

WHAT'S MISSING?

Fruits, vegetables and cereals are commonly thought to be high in essential nutrients, but the majority of today's farming produce is grown in depleted soil, doused with pesticides and stored for long periods of time before being sold. This means that, despite the apparent plenty of our food supply, many people in Europe and the US are suffering from a lack of basic nutrients in our everyday meals.

Studies comparing the nutritional profile of today's food to that grown in the 1940s, before industrial farming became the norm, paint a startling picture:

POTATOES

30% less magnesium
35% less calcium
45% less iron
47% less copper

CARROTS

75% less magnesium
48% less calcium
46% less iron
75% less copper

BROCCOLI (boiled)

75% less calcium

SPINACH (boiled)

60% less iron
96% less copper

SWEDE

71% less iron

ALL MEATS

41% less calcium
54% less iron

ALL FRUITS

27% less zinc

KEY TO COMPOST

THERE ARE SEVERAL WAYS TO IMPROVE AND MAINTAIN THE QUALITY OF YOUR SOIL: MULCHING, GREEN MANURE, CROP ROTATION, NOT WALKING ON IT OR DIGGING IT, AND, OF COURSE, COMPOSTING. THE MORE YOU GROW YOUR OWN THE MORE FAMILIAR YOU WILL FIND YOURSELF WITH THESE TECHNIQUES. BUT IF YOU ARE NEW TO GARDENING AND WANT TO GET STARTED IN A QUICK CLIMATE-FRIENDLY WAY THEN BEGIN BY LEARNING TO COMPOST.

Composting is nature's way of recycling. Making a compost heap is an effective thing that anyone with a garden can do today. Some local councils even supply compost heap containers at a heavily discounted rate in order to encourage recycling and cut down on landfill – so there's no reason not to give it a try.

Adding organic matter such as compost to soil also helps store carbon, which is good for the environment. A quarter of the UK's agricultural GHG emissions could be offset by adopting practices such as adding organic matter to the soil, and at a domestic level the principle is exactly the same: our gardens can act as carbon sinks if we look after them properly.

The key to good compost-making is a variety of ingredients that bring different nutrients to the heap and support different kinds of fungi and bacteria. Anything that has once been living can go into the compost heap, and in fact the greater the range of materials the better. Working together, they break down the mixture faster and more effectively. Put it all on the pile and let nature do the rest. Composting is a great way to make your own food scraps part of a domestic 'closed loop' system, which both reduces your household waste and makes use of it. Instead of going to landfill, the waste is broken down and returned to the soil in your garden to help improve its quality. All you need are some basic materials like kitchen scraps and something to accelerate the breaking-down process. Here's how to get started:

WHAT TO USE	ACCELERATORS	AVOID
CARDBOARD AND PAPER	COMFREY	ANIMAL MANURES***
DEAD FLOWERS	COMPOST ACCELERATOR POWDER	CAT AND DOG FAECES DISPOSABLE NAPPIES
EGG BOXES, NEWSPAPER,	GRASS CUTTINGS**	COAL ASH
EGG SHELLS	NETTLES	DISEASED PLANT MATERIAL
GARDEN VEGETABLE WASTE	SEAWEED (FROM UNPOLLUTED BEACHES)	GLASS
KITCHEN FRUIT AND VEGETABLE WASTE	URINE	GLOSSY PAPER
MUSHROOM COMPOST*		MEAT AND FISH SCRAPS
NON-FLOWERING WEEDS		METAL
SAWDUST, WOOD SHAVINGS		PLASTIC
STRAW AND HAY*		
TEA LEAVES, COFFEE GROUNDS		
WOOD ASH		
WOOL OR FEATHERS*		

* Check that mushroom composts, straw and hay are from organic sources, that wool waste does not contain residues from chemical dips, and that feathers come from acceptable production systems.

If you're concerned about organic gardening you're probably concerned about animal welfare too.
** Grass cuttings should be well mixed in.

*** Some manures are fine. Manure from horses or cows (not from animals fed on GM products) is dry and stable. Pig manure is too cold and wet.

LEAVES

Leaves should be composted separately. They take longer to break down and produce compost that is low in nutrients but excellent for improving soil structure and moisture retention. Normally leaf moulds need to be stacked for two years, enclosed in a simple wire bin, but the process can be speeded up by turning the leaves, chopping them up (try running your lawn mower over them beforehand) or watering them with urine.

CHICKENS

If you keep chickens their droppings can enrich a compost heap. Also, materials that are slower to degrade can be spread in the chicken run for the birds to scratch and peck at. This will help them to break down much faster.

TIPS

Remember to apply your compost to the soil in the growing season; applying in autumn or winter can mean that nutrients are lost in the rains. Compost applied at any time of year, however, will help to improve soil structure.

YOU CAN GROW A SURPRISING AMOUNT OF FOOD ON YOUR ROOF, DECK, PATIO OR WINDOWSILL. THE REWARDS CAN BE BIG, EVEN IF YOUR SPACE IS SMALL. ACCORDING TO THE NATIONAL TRUST, THERE ARE 600 ACRES OF URBAN WINDOW LEDGES AVAILABLE IN THE FIVE MILLION FLATS IN THE UK. THIS AREA IS THE EQUIVALENT OF A GROWING SPACE THE SIZE OF 344 FOOTBALL PITCHES.

The 'green space' created by gardening in areas as small as windowsills or balconies is essential because it creates sheltering areas and stop-off points for insects and birds as they weave their way through our neighbourhoods. Every little bit really does help.

Almost any kind of herb can be grown on a windowsill or patio including fennel, lemon balm, rosemary, peppermint, thyme, chamomile, sage and parsley. But you can also grow salad leaves such as rocket, mizuna, spinach, mustard, rainbow chard and various lettuces and cabbages. Depending on your space you can even grow beetroot, spring onions, chives, tomatoes, chillies, radishes and dwarf French green beans. If you don't have a windowsill, many of these herbs can also be grown in a simple indoor kitchen garden.

If you have a space of four foot by four foot you can plant what is called a square-foot garden, divided into 16 one-foot square 'plots' in which you plant different types of vegetables. Even if you only have a small bit of concrete you can construct a square-foot garden as a raised bed – essentially a shallow wooden or brick box filled with good quality soil and compost. To keep pests and diseases at bay, rotate your crops the way an organic farmer would. Avoid growing the same vegetables in the same square for more than one year out of four (or even six).

If you have even less space, consider growing your vegetables vertically. You'll need a strong structure, such as a trellis or fence, to support your mature vegetables. Once this is in place try growing tomatoes, peas, beans, cucumber, pumpkin and acorn and butternut squashes. You can harvest an amazing amount of produce from such a small space.

ALWAYS ROOM TO GROW

ALL OF THESE CROPS RELY ON HONEYBEES FOR POLLINATION :

OKRA KIWIFRUIT ONION CELERY CARAMBOLA BEET RAPESEED
BROCCOLI CAULIFLOWER CABBAGE BRUSSELS SPROUTS
CHINESE CABBAGE TURNIP MUSTARD CARAWAY SAFFLOWER
CHESTNUT WATERMELON TANGERINE TANGELO COFFEE
HAZELNUT CANTALOUPE CUCUMBER SQUASH PLANT QUINCE
CARROT BUCKWHEAT STRAWBERRY SOYBEAN COTTON
SUNFLOWER WALNUT FLAX LYCHEE LUPINE MACADAMIA APPLE

BEE FRIENDLY

ALFALFA CACTUS AVOCADO LIMA BEAN SCARLET RUNNER
BEAN PLUM CHERRY APRICOT ALMOND PEAR BOYSENBERRY
RASPBERRY BLACKBERRY REDWOOD SEQUOIA TOMATO
AUBERGINE WHITE CLOVER ALSIKE CLOVER CRIMSON CLOVER
RED CLOVER ARROWLEAF CLOVER BLUEBERRY ALFALFA BROAD
BEAN GRAPE ELDERBERRY BLACKCURRANT REDCURRANT
POMEGRANATE GUAVA PEACH NECTARINE KIDNEY BEAN
HARICOT BEAN ADZUKI BEAN MUNG BEAN STRING BEAN
MANGO CARDAMOM COCONUT AND MORE.

IMAGINE A WORLD WITHOUT ALL OF THOSE...

THE ROLE OF BEES IN THE WORLD'S NATURAL ORDER IS CRUCIAL AND THEIR IMPORTANCE AS POLLINATORS, BOTH FOR AGRICULTURE AND FOR WILD PLANTS, CAN'T BE UNDERESTIMATED. IN THE UK THEY ARE RESPONSIBLE FOR THE POLLINATION OF AROUND £200 MILLION WORTH OF FOOD CROPS PER YEAR. IN THE US BEES ANNUALLY POLLINATE MORE THAN USD$14 BILLION WORTH OF CROPS — MOSTLY FRUITS, VEGETABLES AND NUTS.

FACT:
Of the 256 native bee species in the UK, 25% are now listed as endangered.

But the value of bees to mankind can't simply be quantified in monetary terms. Bees are what are known as a 'keystone' species, ensuring the continued reproduction and survival not only of plants but other organisms that depend on those plants for survival. Once a keystone species disappears, other species begin to disappear too. This is why we have to make every garden as bee friendly as possible.

In recent years, there has been a catastrophic disappearance of bees from their colonies in the US, which has become known as Colony Collapse Disorder (CCD). The most striking symptom of CCD is that the bees appear to die away from the hive. One day they fly away and never return. Those few that are left behind can be carrying five or six viruses, as well as several fungal infections, in their bodies.

Bees have been declining at an alarming rate in the UK too. According to a survey carried out by the British Beekeepers' Association, 33% of the UK's 240,000 honeybee hives were lost in the winter and spring of 2008. The reasons for this decline is complex and not yet fully understood. One major problem is the issue of intensive agricultural practices, including monoculture farming and the use of certain pesticides, including herbicides that kill off plants on which bees forage.

In particular, neonicotinoid insecticides, used on a variety of crops in the UK, have been identified as a significant factor in the drop in Britain's bee numbers. A recent comprehensive study carried out jointly by the Soil Association and the insect research body Buglife has shown that neonicotinoids damage the health and life cycle of bees by attacking the nervous system. The neonicotinoid Imidacloprid, for instance, can cause bees to forget where their hives are located.

The French government banned Imidacloprid in 1999 due to its toxicity to bees, the effects of which French beekeepers labelled 'mad bee disease'. In 2008, Germany, Italy and Slovenia banned all neonicotinoids in response to the honeybee crisis. The Soil Association has been very active in campaigning to have them banned or suspended in the UK where they are still widely used (see petition at **http://apps.soilassociation.org/ Bees/Register.aspx**).

By contrast, organic farms are a haven for bee populations, with their lack of pesticides and their focus on natural ecosystems and native species. They also provide wild spaces at field margins and in hedgerows, which provide a diversity of flowers and habitats for bees to nest in and shelter.

To help give the bee population a boost yourself why not consider maintaining a hive of your own? You don't need acres of land. A small garden or terrace can house a small hive. The UK has many local beekeeping groups who can provide advice and equipment to help you get started.

GROW WILD

A KEY WAY TO MAKE OUR COUNTRYSIDE MORE BEE FRIENDLY – IN FACT MORE FRIENDLY TO NATIVE WILDLIFE OF ALL KINDS – IS TO CONVERT AT LEAST PART OF YOUR GARDEN INTO A WILDLIFE PATCH.

Fill it with bee friendly plants such as sage, lavender, rosemary, mint and nettles – all useful culinary choices too – as well as clovers, sweet peas, forget-me-nots, snowdrops, crocuses, cornflowers, fennel, heathers and trees such as willow, hazel and mimosa, and fruit trees like apples and pears. The more variety the better since we have many different native species of bee in the UK and each depends on different plants for survival.

If you also have room for a small pond with shallow edges – a square metre or so will do – so much the better. Leave the pond to colonise naturally – don't stock it with plants, fish or other animals. Just plant some native species around the edge and watch it come alive with pond skaters, water boatmen, newts, frogs, toads, damsel flies, dragonflies and more.

If you're lucky you may attract some of the UK's 10 most rare pond species: tadpole shrimp, spangled water beetle, starfruit, brown galingale, fairy shrimp, lesser silver water beetle, tassel stonewort, three-lobed water-crowfoot, white-faced darter dragonfly and natterjack toad.

Like windowsills, garden ponds create a network of havens and stop-off points for these creatures, many of which are declining in numbers due to loss of habitat. Many of the insects and amphibians attracted to ponds are gardeners' friends, munching up aphids and caterpillars more effectively than chemical sprays.

A wildlife friendly garden can be beautiful to look at, is low maintenance and contributes to an essential aspect of garden ecology. It encourages the natural cycles of decay and regeneration as well as acting as a haven for the wildlife squeezed out onto the margins by large-scale farming.

MAKE THEM FEEL AT HOME IN YOUR GARDEN

BIRDS
BATS
OWLS
PUT UP
NESTING
BOXES

BEES
HOLES OF DIFFERENT
SIZES DRILLED INTO AN
OLD PIECE OF WOOD CAN
PROVIDE NESTING SITES

FROGS
TOADS
NEWTS
PILE UP LOGS OF DEAD
WOOD FOR THEM TO
SHELTER UNDER

CALL TO ACTION

ACT NOW

- Grow your own — even if it's on a window ledge.
- Take a course in natural pest control and make your garden an organic haven.
- Start making your own jams, pickles and preserves from the food you grow.
- Get composting.
- Make pots and growing tubs from recycled things such as old baskets, cracked teapots, buckets, nappy pails and even tyres.

ACT TOGETHER

- Join a gardening club, or form one yourself.
- Get the family to help you dig a garden pond.
- Swap seeds with your friends and neighbours.
- Help your kids to grow a pizza garden.

ACT DIFFERENTLY

- Harvest rainwater in a water butt and use it on your garden.
- Keep bees and make your own honey.
- Put up nesting boxes for birds, bats and owls.
- Rescue a battery hen and give it a better life in your garden and enjoy fresh eggs and (for some) a source of meat. See the Battery Hen Welfare Trust at **www.bhwt.org.uk**
- Give your surplus produce to someone who needs it.

A GROW-YOUR-OWN ADVENTURE CAN EXTEND TO ANIMALS TOO. ACROSS THE UK THERE'S BEEN A RESURGENCE IN PEOPLE KEEPING CHICKENS IN THEIR BACK GARDENS AS CONCERN ABOUT THE QUALITY OF EGGS FROM BATTERY HENS HAS INCREASED.

Keeping a few chickens provides quality assurance for eggs and, for some, a useful source of meat. Chicken huts and runs are now available in all shapes and sizes to suit whatever space you have.

Chickens can also become part of a closed loop of nutrient recycling in your garden. Their droppings can enrich a compost heap and they can scratch and peck at materials that are slow to degrade to help break them down faster. Given the freedom to roam around your garden hens will also help keep insects, slugs and snails under control.

Currently about 500,000 UK households keep chickens. You can buy your hens at a local farm or, even better, consider rescuing a battery hen from an otherwise dismal life. This has become so popular that in 2008 more than 60,000 battery hens were given a new and better life in back gardens. The Battery Hen Welfare Trust facilitates the rehousing of thousands of battery hens each year and has collection points all over the country. If you've got the room and the inclination why not investigate one of the UK's fastest growing self-sufficiency trends?

CHICKS RULE

A SHORT WORD
with Monty Don

President of the Soil Association, television presenter,
writer and speaker on horticulture

GROW TO EAT

IT MIGHT SEEM STRANGE THAT A GARDENER IS WRITING ON FOOD SECURITY AND OUR NATION'S CULTURAL APPROACH TO FOOD.

The trend has been for gardens to become smaller and smaller and for fewer and fewer people to grow their own vegetables, while food production and food supply has been encouraged into the hands of bigger and bigger growers and companies. We readily talk about the food 'industry' with the same grandiose corporate zeal as oil or chemical industries.

Initially, the global food industry and the back garden potterer scarcely seem to meet, either in concept or in practice. Large growers regard gardening as a domestic leisure activity that has no relationship to 'real' food production or – even more disparagingly – the real world.

When I was chatting recently to a farm contractor in Herefordshire, I told him about my little single 48 horse power (hp) tractor. He looked at me pityingly before telling me that he had just taken delivery of ten 250hp tractors. 'That's the real world of farming, Monty. That's the future,' he said.

Apart from being yet another 'real world' that I have spent my life failing to take part in, I am sure that he is wrong on both counts. I very much doubt if big tractors will be his or anyone's future and I am certain that 'the real world' – the real growing, food world – exists in the back garden just as much as in the 100-acre potato field. Of course, this works both ways, and just as this farmer doesn't see the importance of the garden vegetable patch, I suspect that the vast majority of British gardeners never get closer to a farm than viewing it through their car window.

To my mind, both attitudes are wrong and inappropriate. We need to harness the skills and resources of gardeners as part of our national food supply and integrate it into our whole approach to life. If we do not, then the entire business of feeding ourselves healthily and economically will suffer, along with the social and mental health of the nation, with potentially dire consequences.

It's not as though the situation was not already chaotic. Oil, and all who sail in, on and around her – including much of our food – is more expensive, while houses have fallen in value and the average bank is imploding. What was once a worrying situation has now become a full blown crisis.

Governments are reacting to this by claiming that there's nothing they can do but watch in horror with the rest of us. It's as though they have a set of trusted spanners they've been using for years to maintain and fix the machine and now they find that none of them work.

The truth is that governments are a bigger part of the problem than they can be of the solution. The problem is essentially a failure of trust – of politicians, banks, scientists, our food supply – even, dare I say it, of organic growers. We are in a crisis of trust and nothing and no one is immune to the effects of it. However, there is much that we can do as individuals and small groups rather than as governments or large, unwieldy corporations.

SMALL IS NOT JUST BEAUTIFUL BUT ESSENTIAL

More and more of us are becoming familiar with the insane horror of modern food production – the rape of the rainforests for soya and sugar to fatten meat and people; the intensive feedlots for cattle so stuffed with indigestible grain that their livers corrode and burst; the tonnes of good vegetables that are rejected daily for not being straight enough or pretty enough; the thousands of acres of plastic covering beautiful farmland growing unseasonal fruit in sterile soil.

And then there is the almost unimaginable figure of the estimated 20 million tonnes (based on Lord Haskin's figures) of good food wasted each year in this country between producers, supermarkets and consumers. Even the Waste and Resources Action Programme's (WRAP) smaller figure of 8.3 million tonnes of 'avoidable' food waste in the home – purchased at a value of £12 billion – is deeply shocking.

On top of this are the health costs of our over-processed diet. The NHS spends billions on food-related and food-induced diseases, and today up to one third of children in the UK is obese or overweight. But those who are most vulnerable are the poor, harassed and helpless, the tens of thousands of degraded, cheap, immigrant labourers and the shadowy underclass servicing our comfortable packaged lives. It is they who suffer most.

Shame on us. Not just the supermarkets and the hustlers and the inept governments, but us for being part of this. It has to change. We have to change ourselves.

Over the past 50 years our knowledge, experience and skills on growing, preparing and eating good food have been deliberately abused in the name of commercial profits. By and large, successful food businesses have been directly antagonistic to good food. That is, food that nourishes planet, body and soul. Food that belongs to, and is an important part of, a thriving and balanced society. Food that is based upon equality and openness, and food that is shared with generosity and ritual.

In this respect no other moment in my lifetime has been so fraught with potential catastrophe nor filled with such promise of real, beneficial change. We have a chance to make our food personal again.

Awareness and appreciation of good, healthy food has to begin at home. The very best food belongs first and foremost in the kitchen cupboard and fridge and on our daily tables, and not as an exception in the fancier restaurants or delicatessens, as a treat or as medicine. I would love everybody to have access to and share this basic experience every single day. It can happen, and the first step is for all of us, ordinary consumers, to use our extraordinary powers, in all the modesty of our back gardens.

"*Awareness and appreciation of good, healthy food has to begin at home. The very best food belongs first and foremost in the kitchen.*"

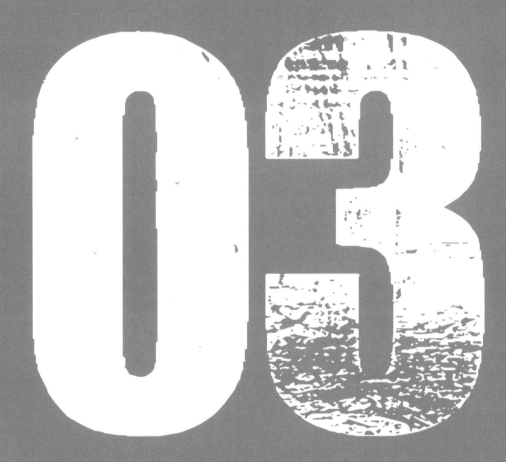

03
COMMUNITY

THE EROSION OF LOCAL COMMUNITIES HAS LED TO THE
DESTRUCTION OF LOCAL FOOD SUPPLIES. THE DECLINE OF THE
HIGH STREET, THE LOSS OF LOCAL MARKETS AND SHOPS, SEEM
UNSTOPPABLE, BUT IT'S NOT. MORE AND MORE COMMUNITIES
ARE BEGINNING TO REBUILD THEMSELVES BY STRENGTHENING
THEIR LINKS TO THE LAND AND THE LOCAL ECONOMY.

A COMMUNITY IS MADE UP OF NETWORKS OF RELATIONSHIPS BETWEEN INDIVIDUALS AND BETWEEN GROUPS AS THEY GO ABOUT FULFILLING THEIR EVERYDAY NEEDS – SUCH AS FOOD, SHELTER AND TRANSPORT.

For these relationships to be sustainable all parties have to work together and understand their interdependence. A community could be described as a human ecosystem where each part feeds into and is dependent on the whole.

One of the oldest forms of human interdependence is our relationship with the land and our food supply. In a globalised world, local communities and their local food chains are rapidly being destroyed. A few years ago this destruction appeared unstoppable.

The growth of supermarkets in the past 40 years has become central to the way we live. The 24/7, one-stop-shop approach to buying food has suited a high-earning, motorised, urban population working ever-increasing hours. Today, the 'big 4' supermarkets (Tesco, Asda, Sainsbury's and Morrisons) sell around two-thirds of food in the UK. This market power has sometimes been a force for good – in recent years supermarkets have increasingly offered a range of ethical products, giving the general public greater access to organic and fairly traded foods.

But this growth has not come without consequences: choosing to shop at the supermarket rather than in the high street has meant the loss of many local stores, and the homogenisation of those that remain. The enormous buying power of supermarkets has pushed cost and environmental impact 'somewhere else', usually to developing countries; and it has brought about significant changes to the landscape of our cities and towns as superstores are located on the urban periphery.

MAKING CONNECTIONS

But many communities today are taking action and working to restore that sense of interdependence through exciting new initiatives. These range from community supported farms and gardens to food buying groups, cooperatives and a renewed commitment to allotments. Some people have gone further to create Transition Town groups, which address all aspects of community life though a range of coordinated projects. They strive to rebuild the resilience that communities have lost as a result of cheap oil and to reduce dramatically their carbon emissions and dependence on fossil fuel. These community enterprises renew and strengthen our links to the land to the lasting benefit of all.

The big picture of why all this is important can be hard to take in. In a busy world where many of us identify ourselves as 'global citizens' the concept of 'community' may even seem a little old fashioned. But, in fact, a great deal of our day-to-day well-being is rooted in how effectively our neighbourhoods, schools, workplaces, cities and towns support us and how well we support them in return.

There is sometimes a reluctance to talk about communities in terms of relationships; a belief that it's too 'touchy feely'. And yet these relationships are vital. Most of the solutions for making communities more sustainable – not just in a food sense – have to do with how people work together one-to-one and as groups, whether it is in local council committees or digging side by side on allotments, in food buying and selling groups or on community supported farms, gardens and orchards.

One of the powerful things about local communities rooted in real relationships is that they begin to build their own networks from the ground up, often without reference to government bodies. They also form supportive systems that feed all aspects of community life. But perhaps the most important thing about the reinvention of community and grass-roots movements like Transition Towns is the way they bring big issues like food security, ecology, climate change and peak oil back into the local community where people feel more empowered to do something about them.

COMMUNITY SUPPORTED FARMS AND GARDENS

THE PHRASE COMMUNITY SUPPORTED AGRICULTURE (CSA) MAY NOT ROLL OFF THE TONGUE LIKE 'ORGANIC' AND 'BIODYNAMIC', INSPIRING VISIONS OF A BRIGHT NEW TOMORROW, BUT DON'T BE FOOLED. THIS WAY OF PRODUCING, BUYING AND SELLING FRESH ORGANIC FOOD TO COMMUNITIES THROUGHOUT THE UK IS ONE OF THE MOST RADICAL AND EXCITING TRENDS IN LOCAL FOOD SYSTEMS. IT RECOGNISES THAT WE CAN NO LONGER AFFORD THE LUXURY OF BEING DISLOCATED FROM OUR FOOD SUPPLY AND AIMS TO FORM PARTNERSHIPS BETWEEN FARMERS AND THE LOCAL COMMUNITY. THESE PROVIDE MULTIPLE MUTUAL BENEFITS, NOT LEAST ENABLING PEOPLE TO RECONNECT TO THE LAND WHERE THEIR FOOD IS GROWN.

The kind of initiatives that come under the CSA umbrella range from a box scheme, where you receive a box of vegetables throughout the year direct from a local supplier, to working with your friends and neighbours to turn a disused plot of local land into a community farm. CSAs can be established in rural and urban areas and in the past few years there has been an explosion of interest, particularly in cities (see also Chapter 5). In the last two years alone the group Making Local Food Work – a collaboration between the Campaign to Protect Rural England, Co-operatives UK, Country Markets Ltd, The National Farmers' Retail and Markets Association (FARMA), The Plunkett Foundation, Sustain and the Soil Association – has helped to establish dozens of schemes throughout the UK (see **www. makinglocalfoodwork.co.uk**).

There is no fixed way of organising a CSA. What works for one community may not work for another so they tend to be flexible and responsive to local needs. As a result, no two CSAs are likely to be run the same way or to sell the same produce. Some CSAs are farmer-run and the farmer manages the production and distribution of food; some are community-run, where a community group hires someone to grow the food, or invests in a small farm, or does the farming itself. Some are a mixture of both. Some focus on providing vegetables, some on fruit and vegetables, a few also aim to provide grains and pulses, as well as meat and dairy. In each case, though, the investment is directed into a project before the food is available, with a view to reaping the rewards at harvest time.

By focusing on providing local food CSAs greatly reduce the links in the supply chain; they cut costs right across distribution, transport, retail and marketing and this cost-cutting is passed directly on to the consumer. It has been shown that produce from CSA projects can be less expensive than the organic produce you buy in the supermarket and a lot fresher as well. In addition, many CSAs have schemes that offer people on a lower income substantial discounts.

The issue of cost is important since most people think that if they buy food from either a CSA or a farmers' market they will have to pay even more of a premium for it. That belief, however, comes from the supermarket experience where consumers can pay up to 40% more for organic produce.

SOME OF THE KEY BENEFITS OF FORMING A CSA ARE:

- receiving fresh food from a source that you know
- fewer 'food miles', less packaging and more ecologically sensitive farming that also ensures improved animal welfare
- a local economy enhanced by higher employment, more local processing, local consumption and a re-circulation of money in the community through 'local spend'

- educating people about varieties of food, its production methods and costs
- having an influence over the local landscape and encouraging more sustainable farming.

There are benefits for farmers too since they receive a more secure income and a higher and fairer return for their produce from selling direct to the public. They also have increased involvement in the local community and the opportunity to respond directly to customers' needs. In addition to offering a workable model of local and seasonal food production, CSAs are a unique way of reskilling people for the coming transition to a post-peak oil lifestyle.

AN ALTERNATIVE ECONOMY

Community initiatives like CSAs represent more than just a shot in the arm for our community spirit. They are a fundamental transformation of our food supply chains and they challenge the supremacy of the globalised economy. If one person trades their excess tomatoes for another person's eggs (for example, through a LETs scheme, where time and goods are used for barter rather than money), or someone helps you work your allotment for a share of the produce, or one buying

group trades its excess for another buying group's excess, they are participating in a system of trade that constitutes an alternative approach to economy. Nobody really knows how to account for such an alternative yet. Some Transition Towns (**www.transitiontowns.org**) even issue their own currencies, a potent symbol of this economic radicalisation. The new economics foundation project Local Alchemy (**http://localalchemy.org**) supports individuals and groups in re-inventing their local economy in a way that encourages spending, and respending, in the community by opening up local employment and business opportunities.

Stepping outside of normal supply chains and economies is courageous, bold, creative, inspiring and certainly political. The reason why such systems continue to thrive, even today as our politicians strive for an evermore globalised society, is that they work. Local systems are flexible: if I don't have my usual type of apple, then maybe my neighbour will have the kind I need, and we'll all get to make our apple crumbles. That flexibility is the key to longer-term sustainability and a fairer share for everyone.

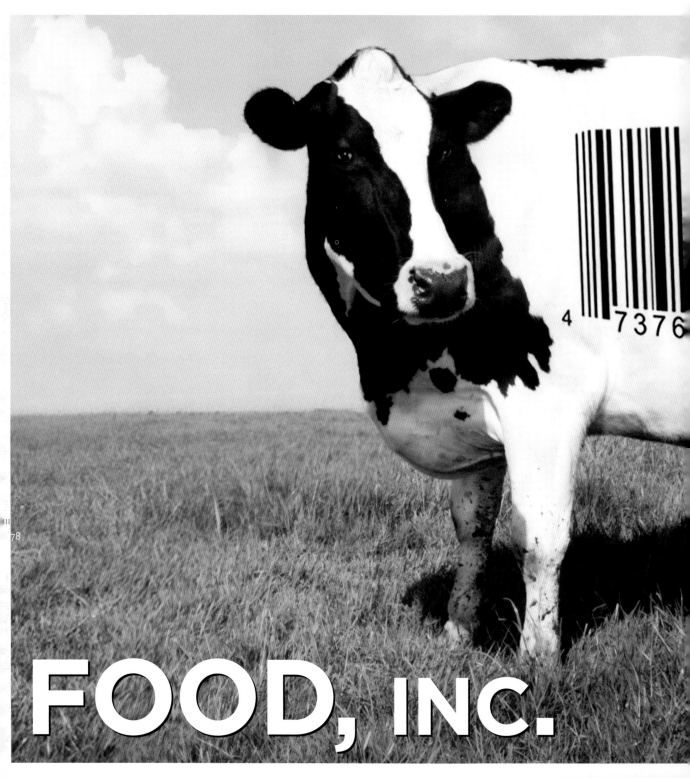

FOOD, INC.

YOU'LL NEVER LOOK AT DINNER THE SAME WAY

SUPERMARKETS HAVE BECOME SO CENTRAL TO THE WAY WE BUY FOOD THAT WE ARE BARELY AWARE OF HOW THEY DIRECT OUR FOOD CHOICES, AND DISCONNECT US FROM THE ORIGINS OF THE THINGS WE BUY. ACCORDING TO THE FOOD ACTIVIST MICHAEL POLLAN THE WAY SUPERMARKETS ARE LAID OUT HAS A HUGE PSYCHOLOGICAL INFLUENCE ON THE WAY WE SHOP. FRESH FOOD FOR INSTANCE, IS OFTEN ON THE PERIPHERY OF THE LAYOUT, OR TOO HIGH UP OR TOO LOW DOWN FOR MOST OF US TO BOTHER TO STRETCH OR BEND TO PICK IT UP.

The supermarket experience can be made more sustainable, however, by making more careful food choices once you are there. First of all make a list of fresh foods you want before you go, and stick to that. Use labels well – organic and fairtrade certification, as well as countries of origin, tell you something useful about the provenance and the 'journey' of your food and can help you make better decisions. Avoiding products with multiple unpronounceable ingredients is also important; likewise, foods that make health claims are usually highly packaged and highly processed and completely unnecessary if you have a good diet of fresh food.

Even if you need or enjoy the convenience of supermarkets, it's still worth diversifying the way you shop to include other food outlets from time to time.

FARMERS' MARKETS

At many farmers' markets you will be buying direct from producers who grow food within 30 miles of your home (100 miles if you live in a big city). Contrast this with the hundreds or even thousands of miles that much supermarket produce travels to reach your table.

You can also talk to the people who produce your food, ask questions about it and provide feedback – good or bad – direct to the suppliers. The money you spend in the market goes to the people who actually do the work to produce the food, rather than a chain of

middlemen. That simple investment on your part helps support the small family farms that are rapidly disappearing from our food landscape: between 1993 and 2002 more than 100,000 farmers and farm workers in the UK left farming.

Most farmers' markets sell a high proportion of organic and/or biodynamically produced foods. Some are totally organic. Well organised ones can provide most of your weekly food needs, and some even sell fairly traded coffee, chocolate and tea. What gets sold depends on the vision of the person or group that sets it up.

Because the food you buy in these markets will have been harvested only a few days before, it will also be some of the freshest you can find – and this means it will have retained more of its valuable nutrients. Because it is produced locally the food will be seasonal, which means that in springtime there may not be tomatoes but there will be peas and broad beans and in winter there may not be strawberries but there will be apples and quince. And as your fresh food supply becomes more varied, so will your skills in the kitchen providing day-to-day menus bursting with flavour.

If you don't have a farmers' market in your area you can set one up. Many villages and towns use school playgrounds as a good, convenient place to host them. See **www. farmersmarkets.net** and **www. farmshopping.net** to find a genuine farmers' market near you.

BETTER BUYING

NINETY PER CENT OF US STILL SHOP IN SUPERMARKETS ON A WEEKLY BASIS.

CONVENIENT AND FRESH

BOX SCHEMES

Save food miles and have fresh organic produce delivered to your home. There are now about 600 box schemes in the UK that can bring food direct from the farm straight to your door. It pays to do your homework and decide whether you want produce that comes from your local or regional area, direct from the farm or through a wholesaler.

With a box scheme customers usually sign up to regular weekly or fortnightly deliveries. Sometimes you can choose the day your produce is delivered and some schemes also supply other farm goods such as meat, dairy and cereals. To find a box scheme in your area log on to **www.soilassociation. org/buydirect/aspx**

FACT:
For every £10 spent on an organic box scheme, £24 is generated in the local economy; and by comparison, every £10 spent in a supermarket generates £12 for the local food economy.

FACT:
By keeping money circulating in local economies, we can create more jobs, support community cohesion and have a smaller ecological footprint.

SET UP A FOOD BUYING GROUP

Cooperatives or food groups that buy produce in bulk and direct from farmers, wholesalers or social enterprises can be as small as a few neighbours or as large as a whole community.

Group members usually live near each other and share a delivery between them. Most groups have, at the least, an informal agreement about how things are organised, and some have a formal legal structure, as in the case of a true cooperative.

Until recently there weren't many practical resources available for those trying to start or become part of a food co-op. But now you can get good advice from the Soil Association, Sustain and Making Local Food Work. Some things to consider include:

- **Planning:** what do you want to do, who is going to organise it and how much will it all cost (for boxes, bags, promotional material and wastage)?

- **Membership:** the more members you have the more buying power you have. You can draw these from friends, neighbours, community centres and parents at your child's school.

- **Produce:** what do you want to buy (fruit and vegetables, meats or wholefoods) and who do you want to buy it from (wholesalers, local producers or community growing schemes)?

- **Premises:** where will the food be delivered, stored and distributed?

- **Funding and other resources:** you may need order forms, tills, computer programmes, delivery vehicles and some start-up cash.

- **Permits:** check with your local authority. You will need to register as a food business with the local environmental health department if you are running more than five days in a five-week period.

Although they have increased in popularity recently there's nothing new about food buying groups. In the 1970s as the health foods movement and concerns about poor quality processed foods began to grow, so did the popularity of food co-ops. More recently, community-based food groups have also been set up to give people on low incomes, or those living in areas with few shops, access to more affordable and better quality fruit and vegetables.

Whatever your reason for becoming part of a food buying group, ordering in bulk direct from farmers and other suppliers ensures that more of us can buy their fresh, locally grown food at an affordable price.

For more information, visit
www.makinglocalfoodwork.co.uk
www.sustainweb.org

PROVIDING AN ALLOTMENT – A PARCEL OF LAND THAT INDIVIDUALS CAN USE TO GROW THEIR OWN FOOD – FOR EVERYONE WHO WANTS ONE SHOULD BE A NATIONAL PRIORITY. LOCAL AUTHORITIES IN ENGLAND AND WALES DO HAVE A LEGAL OBLIGATION TO PROVIDE 15 ALLOTMENTS PER 1,000 HOUSEHOLDS WITH NO MORE THAN SIX PEOPLE WAITING FOR A PLOT AT ANY ONE TIME. IN REALITY, MOST LOCAL COUNCILS ARE STRUGGLING TO MEET THIS OBLIGATION AS DEMAND FOR ALLOTMENTS HAS INCREASED IN RECENT YEARS.

Allotments are crucial to the goal of sustainable development for towns and cities. They are important 'green lungs' for urban areas, and provide valuable habitats for all kinds of creatures. They are wildlife corridors linking wild spaces and making these accessible to the animals and insects that need to reach them. Some allotment groups even manage separate areas for wildlife and many use organic techniques for growing their produce, working with nature rather than against it. Some experiment with permaculture to make the best use of available land, light and water, to achieve better yields and provide the most diverse habitat possible.

The traditional image of older men in flat caps simply does not apply on today's allotments, which attract a diversity of people. Today's allotment enthusiast is likely to be a younger woman who brings along children to help with the gardening. Allotments can become vibrant community spaces where different cultural skills are brought together and shared. In Birmingham many West African families grow traditional foods such as chillies and yams, while in parts of London and Leicestershire Indian families grow okra, cumin and coriander. Growing your own gives you the freedom of choice to grow what you want to.

As well as reconnecting us with the soil and seasons, working an allotment reacquaints us with the notion of real time. There are no shortcuts, no time shifting. A tomato, pumpkin or courgette takes time to grow. Allotments, when you can get hold of one, aren't expensive but they are a more ambitious grow-your-own project than a kitchen or container garden – but the rewards are bigger too.

Allotments were originally intended to help individuals feed themselves. Times change, though. Many people still work them individually, but the size of an allotment plot and the time required to work it can seem daunting. One solution is to share one, as more and more people are now doing – sharing the work and tools but also knowledge, tips, seeds and eventually the fruits of their labours. Working an allotment will never be as simple as buying from the supermarket, but this misses the point: it will be cheaper, healthier, more sociable, more fulfilling and better for the land and the local community.

FINDING SPACE

TO GROW

ALLOTMENT FACTS

- There are around 300,000 allotments in England and Wales. Numbers have been declining due to urban development. In the 1940s there were 1.4 million allotments in the UK.

- More than 100,000 people are currently on waiting lists for allotments. The average waiting time is around three months but in some inner-city areas it can be 10 or even 40 years.

- Plots average 9m by 6m and cost between £6 and £50 per year. Most have concessions for the unemployed and for older people.

- Typical annual yield is around £300 of produce.

- If you are interested in having an allotment contact your local authority. Many provide information about their allotments on their websites, but you should always check out prospective sites for yourself to get a better picture of facilities (toilets, running water, ease of access) and security.

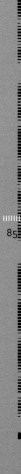

LAND IN THE UK IS AT A PREMIUM

AROUND 70 PER CENT IS OWNED BY

THE WEALTHIEST ONE PER CENT OF THE POPULATION

LANDSHARE SCHEMES

Land in the UK is at a premium. Around 70% is owned by the wealthiest 1% of the population. Allotments, of course, are considered open spaces, but there is more that communities can do to grow their own food in 'closed spaces' also. These include the grounds of schools (see Chapter 4), community halls, churches, hospitals and even prisons.

There have been calls for brownfield (former industrial) sites to be turned into allotments – though this is not always practical or desirable since many of them can be heavily polluted. Some reports have suggested that the Royal Family should make some of its holdings available to the public. Recently the National Trust committed itself to opening up some of its land (either restored kitchen gardens, agricultural land or vacant land near Trust properties) to create 1,000 allotment plots around the country.

In response to this growing desire to work a smallholding, new schemes giving people access to land are being developed across the UK.

A National Landshare Scheme, initiated by chef Hugh Fearnley-Whittingstall, aims to link up people who have spare land with those who want to work it. This could be a garden in a private home that the owners cannot work themselves, or land from farmers and other estate owners who are willing to provide a plot of land in return for a share of the produce harvested.

The Soil Association Land Trust is a new initiative to safeguard land for organic and sustainable farming, in perpetuity. The aim is to build a land bank that is farmed sustainably and offers increased opportunities for community engagement and provides access to land for new farmers. **www.soilassociation.org/ landtrust.aspx**

This kind of organised landsharing can bring local people together in real social networks, as opposed to virtual ones. In Transition Town Totnes, for example, there is a local garden share initiative that puts those with land in touch with those who want to grow their own vegetables. Owners typically receive between one-fifth and one-third of the produce as payment. Visit the Soil Association website **www.soilassociation.org** to find out more.

CALL TO ACTION

Thriving communities don't come about by accident. They usually result from the vision of one or a handful of people who are willing to work hard to inspire others and make them happen.

ACT NOW

- Put your name down for an allotment.

- Sponsor an apple tree and harvest its fruit.

- Rent a plot of farmland and have vegetables grown on your behalf.

- Buy shares in a cow and receive interest in cheese.

- Rent a vine from one of Britain's few vineyards.

- Dedicate a plot of organic land to be farmed sustainably in perpetuity – see **www.soilassociation.org/landtrust.aspx**

ACT TOGETHER

- Take your children to a pick-your-own farm.

- Get together with neighbours to form a food buying group.

- Help preserve and revive community orchards by forming a group and planting fruit trees somewhere in your neighbourhood.

- Turn unused or abandoned land in your area into a community farm or garden.

- Get your community group to make a 'food map' that details producers, farmers, growers, processors, distributors and retailers in your local area – useful for understanding what you do and don't have access to locally.

- Join a Transition network or set up your own Transition Town – see **www.transitiontowns.org**

ACT DIFFERENTLY

- Try buying your produce from a farmers' market, farm shop or cooperative.

- Put any spare garden space you have up on a landshare board **http://landshare.channel4.com**

- Volunteer to help with the running of an organic farm or a farm shop and get paid in food.

- Think Slow Food instead of fast food. The global Slow Food movement is committed to promoting the diversity of local and regional quality food. It also guarantees farmers a fair price and protects the environment and the natural landscape. See **www.slowfood.org.uk**

- Grow your own.

- Set up a CSA – see **www.soilassociation.org/CSA.aspx**

COMMUNITY ORCHARDS

Allotments tend to be about growing vegetables. If it's fruit you're interested in, why not help preserve or even plant a community orchard? Orchards were once widespread throughout the UK, but in the last quarter of a century the amount of land devoted to fruit growing has declined by 64%. The group Common Ground (**www. commonground.org.uk**) is now spearheading a campaign to revive our interest in orchards, not only as productive gardens, but as community resources.

The idea is to maintain large open spaces with fruit trees planted among grass and wildflowers. These spaces are open to the public at all times and maintained by volunteers who share in the harvest. Orchards can be used as camping grounds, for nature conservation, school trips, horticultural training and reskilling, and for local festivities.

Community orchards work well in both town and country. New orchards can be established on housing and industrial estates and in schools and hospitals. Local people run them and decide how they are used. Profit is not the main goal, though they can pay for themselves with income generated from fruit sales.

Supermarkets claim that they are committed to stocking more British varieties of fruit, but the reality is very different. Apples are a good example. Over the centuries there have been more than 2,000 varieties of apple cultivated in the UK. Today only 30 varieties of British apple are grown for commercial purposes, and supermarkets, on average, stock perhaps four or five.

Our local apple heritage includes varieties with names like Peasgood Nonsuch, Bloody Ploughman and Greasy Pippin, Laxton's Superb, Lady's Finger of Offaly and Kentish Fillbasket. Some varieties, like the Knobby Russett or the Ashmeads Kernel, may not achieve the cosmetic perfection required for supermarkets but you can still find them in farmers' markets and other, less aesthetically demanding outlets. Reviving a community orchard can help preserve and protect our stock of indigenous fruit trees for future generations.

If you don't have an area of land large enough to create an orchard, use your community gardens. Encourage friends and neighbours to plant a couple of fruit trees each and together you can create a village or street orchard.

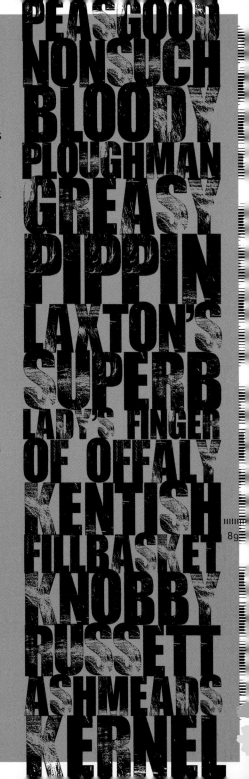

PEASGOOD NONSUCH BLOODY PLOUGHMAN GREASY PIPPIN LAXTON'S SUPERB LADY'S FINGER OF OFFALY KENTISH FILLBASKET KNOBBY RUSSETT ASHMEADS KERNEL

A SHORT WORD
with Rob Hopkins

Co-founder of the Transition Network
and Transition Town Totnes

TIME FOR TRANSITION

WE ONCE BELIEVED THAT FOOD WAS SOMETHING GROWN NEAR WHERE YOU LIVED, BY SOMEONE YOU KNEW, AND THAT IT WAS COOKED IN YOUR OWN KITCHEN.

The steady and relentless erosion of this idea began after the Second World War and accelerated during the 1960s and 1970s. New subsidies and international trade agreements, accompanied by the rise of the supermarket and the dazzling possibility of having any food you wanted from anywhere in the world, systematically changed the logic of our food economy.

It became, perversely, cheaper and easier to buy food grown many hundreds of miles away than food grown up the road. Small-scale farmers and growers went out of business and their land was absorbed into larger farms. Orchards were grubbed out. Our lives became saturated with processed foods and our waistlines started to bulge. The illusion of plenty came at a cost, as we discarded into the recycling bin of history a complex, highly skilled, adaptable and place-specific system. It could be dismantled in a day, but it would take far, far longer to rebuild once it had gone.

Given the need for an urgent and far-reaching rethink of everything we do, what might food and farming look like in the future? If we were able to taste, smell, hear and feel the UK's food system in 2030, what might it be like?

It would, out of necessity, be more focused on local markets, a lower emitter of GHGs and a user of far less water. It would be free of its dependence on artificial fertilisers and chemical pesticides, employ far more people and be supported by a complex web of local processors and retailers. The rural landscape would look far more diverse than it does now: it would be home to a variety of land uses, with more tree cover and less livestock. Soil building would have to become a national obsession, given the powerful role that soil plays in locking up carbon.

One very useful model of a future food system for this country has been developed by Julie Brown of Growing Communities in Hackney, east London. Growing Communities runs a number of food projects across its neighbourhood, including a vegetable box scheme for more than 450 people and a popular organic farmers' market. Based on the Growing Communities experience, Julie has developed what could well become the template for the food systems of the future. The model is a series of concentric rings, starting at the centre with the inner city and working out towards the rest of the world on the outer edge. Julie is starting to explore how her model could be replicated in both urban and non-urban communities.

Ultimately, this is not just about farming, but about a move away from a nation of farmers supplying a nation of passive consumers to one in which consumers grow some of their own food and are linked with local growers. This system would once again value food production as an art and a skill, and treat it with the esteem it lost some 30 or so years ago.

The idea of promoting local food production rather than relying unquestioningly on the globalised food system is not novel or in any way unique. A rich and diverse web of allotment associations, farmers' markets, back-garden growers, food co-ops and seed swappers have existed up and down the country for many years. They form the firm shoulders on which the current work of myriad organisations promoting and implementing local food systems now stand.

City farms can be found in most urban areas, and some artists now see edible landscaping as an art form. The mayor of London, Boris Johnson, has initiated a programme to establish 2,012 food-producing gardens in the capital in time for the 2012 Olympics. Blue Peter recently dug up its garden to put in vegetable beds instead. Manchester City Council is planning to spend £200,000 planting fruits, nuts and vegetables in all the city's parks.

I love my garden. In many ways, I am at my happiest there. In my raised beds, built as terraces on a slope, I grow carrots, beetroots, salads, spinach, chard, onions, kale, beans, peas and much more. Few things taste as good fresh from the garden as carrots and spinach. I don't grow food because I have to. It would, after all, be easier to buy it from the supermarket. I grow food because it feels fantastic to do so – it is a magical, almost alchemical, process that allows me to know what I am feeding my family, and that lets them connect what they eat with the beds they can see while they are eating it.

Similarly, the ideas set out in this book are not hair-shirt responses to impending catastrophe. They have arisen from people finding out that they share ideals and visions, and that they enjoy working together to bring these visions to fruition. These are people who discover that growing some of their own food is a learnable skill, not the metaphysical art they once believed it to be. They find that their kids become enthusiastic about food for the first time, and they feel fitter and more connected to their community and to the soil. They are the desk-bound generation, living in an economy based largely, as the comedian David Mitchell recently observed, on 'ring tones and lattes'. They have discovered the joys of planting out onion sets on a sunny but chilly spring morning. They are people like you and me, who have decided that they want to take back control of what they eat.

> *"The idea of promoting local food rather than relying unquestioningly on a globalised food system is not novel or in any way a new or unique idea."*

04
SCHOOLS

by Rikke Bruntse-Dahl

Food for Life Partnership

SCHOOLS ARE COMMUNITIES IN THEIR OWN RIGHT,
WOVEN FROM NETWORKS OF PUPILS, PARENTS, TEACHERS,
ADMINISTRATORS AND COMMUNITY GROUPS. OUR SCHOOLS
CAN BE MODELS FOR A SUSTAINABLE WORLD. THEY CAN
ALSO BE EFFECTIVE AGENTS OF CHANGE THAT HELP PROVIDE
FUTURE GENERATIONS WITH THE SKILLS THEY NEED TO THRIVE
IN THE FACE OF CLIMATE CHANGE AND PEAK OIL.

FOR MOST OF US, THE QUEST TO CREATE A SUSTAINABLE FUTURE IS LINKED TO A DESIRE TO MAKE THE WORLD A BETTER PLACE FOR OUR CHILDREN. IT MAKES SENSE, THEN, TO LOOK AT SUSTAINABILITY IN TERMS OF LONGEVITY. THIS IS WHERE SCHOOLS COME IN. ONLY BY ENGAGING THE NEXT GENERATION IN THE ISSUES WE FACE AND THE SOLUTIONS TO THEM CAN WE CREATE A FUTURE THAT IS TRULY SUSTAINABLE.

Schools play a key role in this mission, and food can be a central part of their efforts. The curriculum presents endless opportunities to discuss the problems and possibilities in our food system, and provides a platform to teach the skills of growing and cooking food. Schools are in a unique position to ensure that, regardless of geography and background, all children get the opportunity to experience the joy of eating and making food that is good for us and the planet.

As hubs in the local community, schools can reach out not only to parents but to businesses, senior citizens, clubs and organisations. With food, they can use these networks to generate a mechanism for change and drive a transformation of the local food culture. Through practical food education initiatives, such as cooking and gardening clubs, and procurement for school meals, schools can have an immense impact on their wider community, inspiring and leading by example.

Simple scenarios for this include inviting members of the local community to join the children for lunch or to participate in their cooking and gardening clubs. Schools are also ideal for facilitating local farmers' markets and food co-ops, which have wide social benefits. In sourcing produce from neighbouring farms and businesses schools can boost the local economy massively and open up new markets between the producers and the wider community.

In England today, more than 1,500 schools and their communities are transforming their food culture through the Food for Life Partnership programme in an effort to become more sustainable. With more than 130,000 children across England eating school meals that are more local, seasonal and organic, this is already having a massive impact on the national food system.

Globally, these changes can also make a difference. By changing supply chains to reduce the consumption of out-of-season, industrially produced food, schools can shape not only our national food system, but also the international perspective on food production. These efforts demonstrate that we do not need to rely so heavily on fossil fuel-based farming and distribution methods, and that by pulling together in local communities we can achieve a degree of resilience.

WHOSE FUTURE IS IT ANYWAY?

"THE FOOD FOR LIFE PARTNERSHIP IS ABOUT MENDING OUR BROKEN FOOD CULTURE BY INSPIRING THE NEXT GENERATION TO CARE ABOUT WHAT THEY EAT. WE LEARN HOW THE FOOD WE EAT IMPACTS ON OUR HEALTH, THE HEALTH OF OUR PLANET AND ANIMAL WELFARE BY GROWING IT, COOKING IT, EATING IT AND VISITING FARMS." EMMA NOBLE DIRECTOR OF THE FOOD FOR LIFE PARTNERSHIP

The philosophy behind the Food for Life Partnership was inspired by dinner lady Jeanette Orrey. With Jeanette, the Soil Association founded the Food for Life campaign in 2003 to help schools source fresh, local and organic produce and to give pupils the chance to visit farms to see how and where their food is grown or produced.

As the school dinner campaign developed it became clear that food education was needed to ensure that the next generation not only eat well at school, but also take the principles of a healthy food culture with them into adulthood.

The Soil Association therefore joined forces with three other education and food-focused charities: Garden Organic, the Focus on Food Campaign and the Health Education Trust. Together they formed the Food for Life Partnership, which is funded from 2007–11 through a grant from the Big Lottery Fund Well-being Programme.

The Food for Life Partnership comprises a network of schools, communities, caterers and food producers across England who work to transform food culture. Through an awards scheme, the programme provides schools with a framework

and guidance on how to link school meals with growing, cooking, farm visits and community engagement. Dedicated teams also offer hands-on support to school staff who are creating school gardens, caterers working to improve school meals, and farmers who want to host educational visits.

All schools can join the programme for free. To find out more visit www.foodforlife.org.uk

HAPPY
MEALS

THE IMPORTANCE OF IMPROVING THE QUALITY OF SCHOOL MEALS CANNOT BE UNDERESTIMATED. FOR MANY CHILDREN, IT IS THE ONLY HOT MEAL THEY HAVE IN THE DAY. THE STATE OF SCHOOL MEALS IN THE UK WAS A BAD JOKE UNTIL RELATIVELY RECENTLY. REHEATED SAUSAGE ROLLS, TURKEY TWIZZLERS AND CHIPS WERE THE NORM, AS EDUCATION AUTHORITIES PURSUED 'BEST VALUE' THROUGH COST-CUTTING. THESE POLICIES LEFT OUR CHILDREN EATING UNHEALTHY, IN SOME CASES, BARELY EDIBLE FOOD. THEY ALSO GUTTED SCHOOLS OF THEIR FOOD INFRASTRUCTURE, WITH ON-SITE KITCHENS CLOSED AND COOKING OUT-SOURCED TO CHEAPER COMMERCIAL CATERERS.

In the middle of the 2000s things started to change. The work of the Soil Association's Food for Life campaign, and Jamie Oliver's Channel 4 series, raised the issue up the political agenda. In 2005 the government announced new rules for school meals, which led to the introduction of nutrient-based standards in all schools by 2009. These standards are a step forward in ensuring the nutritional quality of school lunches in schools. However, while the standards rightfully concentrate on the health of pupils, the health of the planet has still not been taken into consideration.

School meals should not just be about the health benefits of the food on the plate. They are also a vital part of children's broader education about life. What we feed our children goes a long way to shaping their future ideas of what food should be about. By putting fresh, local, seasonal and organic produce on the school menu, children can make the link between what they are taught in class about healthy, climate-friendly diets and what they are actually eating.

We can also teach them the expectation that food should be freshly prepared and of high quality, which is a crucial step towards creating a sustainable food system. If the central channel of state authority in the children's lives – the school – demonstrates respect and care towards the food it serves, then the children will learn to respect food too.

That's why it's so important that schools think more deeply about the meals they offer – the chicken might be freshly cooked, but if it's a battery hen imported from Thailand, what does that say to children about our values as a society? Pushing schools to source more fresh food, more local food, and higher welfare meat and fish – and then tell their children why they are doing so – is a great way of affecting real change in our wider food culture.

Inculcating this sense of respect towards food in school is not just about the food on the plate. It's also about the space in which it's eaten. Lunch should be a pleasure, not a chore, but too often in schools children are shepherded in and out of the dining hall, served up compartmentalised 'meals' on plastic flight trays, with pudding served next to the starter, all within a strict half hour time limit. Especially for younger children the experience can be difficult and stressful. Perhaps it's no wonder that so many opt out, instead relying on packed lunches that are akin to eating a picnic every day.

Improving children's experience in the dining room is very important in laying the foundation for a good food culture in the future. Along with serving freshly prepared, local, seasonal and organic meals, eating in pleasant surroundings with a focus on manners and developing social skills, play a massively importantly role in giving children a lifelong respect for eating.

CATERING FOR CHANGE

food
for life
PARTNERSHIP

ONE OF THE DIFFICULTIES IN CHANGING SCHOOL FOOD IS OFTEN THE BUREAUCRATIC SYSTEM – THE LOCAL PRIMARY MIGHT BE ONE OF HUNDREDS OF SCHOOLS SERVED BY A SINGLE CATERER – AND MAKING A CHANGE IN ONE SMALL COG OF THE SYSTEM CAN BE DAUNTING. OF COURSE, THE ADVANTAGE OF A BUREAUCRATIC SYSTEM IS THAT IF YOU MAKE CHANGES IN ONE SCHOOL THE EFFECTS ARE AMPLIFIED MANY TIMES OVER.

The health of children as well as the planet is the raison d'être of the Soil Association Food for Life Catering Mark, which hundreds of schools and their caterers have already signed up to. The Mark is split into three tiers – Bronze, Silver and Gold – and allows caterers to make step-wise progress towards greater use of fresh, seasonal, local and organic ingredients, high welfare meat and sustainable fish.

The successes of this approach have been remarkable. For example, the Nottinghamshire County Council caterer was the first local authority caterer in the country to provide all its schools – primary and secondary – with Food for Life Silver standard food, after several schools in Nottingham joined the Food for Life Partnership and started pushing for change. In practice, this means that every day 30,000 children in Nottinghamshire eat school meals that are at least 75% freshly prepared with a range of local and organic ingredients. All chicken, eggs and pork are Freedom Food or free-range, and no fish from unsustainable sources is permitted.

In addition, all children now eat from proper plates, with pudding following the main course. A small, but significant, change.

It's said that the proof of any pudding is in the eating. In 2008 and 2009 the uptake of school meals in Food for Life Partnership award-winning schools increased 16%. Caterers attribute this to the fact that the schools have made healthy and climate-friendly food education an integral part of everyday life. The Catering Mark has been so successful in schools that it is now available to all caterers, including those in hospitals and restaurants. In late 2009, the Sustainable Development Commission – an independent watchdog of the UK government – listed the Food for Life programme as one of three top practical initiatives for promoting a more sustainable food supply.

FOOD FOR LIFE MENU

Schools and caterers involved in the Food for Life Partnership use a tiered approach to improve school meals.

BRONZE SCHOOLS SERVE

- Meals that contain no undesirable food additives and no hydrogenated fats
- 75% of dishes freshly prepared
- Meat that is consistent with UK welfare standards and eggs from cage-free hens
- Seasonal menus
- No GM ingredients

And catering staff are well trained.

SILVER SCHOOLS SERVE

in addition:

- A range of local, organic and fairtrade food
- High welfare chicken, eggs and pork products (at least Freedom Food or free-range)
- No fish from the Marine Conservation Society 'fish to avoid' list

And information is on display about where the food has come from.

GOLD SCHOOLS SERVE

in addition:

- At least 30% of ingredients organic or Marine Stewardship Council certified
- At least 50% of ingredients locally sourced
- Organic meat, dairy products and eggs with a welfare gold standard

Non-meat dishes are promoted as part of a healthy, balanced, climate-friendly diet.

IT'S EASY TO FILL YOUNG MINDS WITH HEALTH MESSAGES, AND SCHOOLS HAVE BEEN DOING IT FOR A WHILE, BUT TO TURN THEORY INTO ACTION CHILDREN NEED SKILLS. KNOWING HOW TO GROW ORGANIC FRUIT AND VEGETABLES AND COOK MEALS FROM SCRATCH IS THE KEY TO ENABLING THEM TO FEED THEMSELVES AND THEIR FAMILIES HEALTHY, CLIMATE-FRIENDLY FOOD.

FOOD

GET GROWING

Growing food organically at school gives children the opportunity to learn about where their fruit and vegetables come from. Young people always show more enthusiasm for eating food that they have grown and nurtured from a seed themselves. As pupils develop their growing skills they become more aware of the diverse varieties of fruit and vegetables they can grow, season by season, and learning how to garden organically they will learn to respect and appreciate the environment and their place in it.

Starting a school garden is as easy as growing a few herbs or tomatoes in containers in the playground. The skills acquired in gardening projects can all be tied into the curriculum as they contribute positively to the overall education of our children. Even inner-city schools with very little outdoor space have found creative ways of maximising growing areas by building raised beds in the playground, placing grow bags and pots in every possible corner and adding window boxes to their window ledges. Other schools have even taken on allotments or joined forces with neighbouring institutions, such as care homes, to acquire land to grow food on.

COOKING UP A STORM

You can make the food in school as wonderful as you like, but it will mean little if these messages aren't reinforced at home. Sadly, many parents – products themselves of our education system – lack an understanding and respect for good food. Schools present a great opportunity to use children as good food ambassadors, taking sustainable eating messages into the wider community through positive pester power. A good place to start is in teaching our children to cook if Mum and Dad are unable (or unwilling) to do so themselves.

Encouraging children to learn how to cook a meal from scratch using fresh produce is an absolute necessity for a sustainable food future. In any case, cooking is a basic life skill that should be an essential part of every child's education.

As well as pushing schools to timetable cooking classes, after-school cooking clubs can be a great way of driving children's enthusiasm for good food. Many Food for Life Partnership schools have also organised clubs where parents can join and cook with their children.

DOWN ON THE FARM

Knowing how food is produced allows our children to make informed food choices as they grow up. Visiting farms is a fun and obvious way of learning about food production. Through the Food for Life Partnership, schools can set up a link with a local organic farm, and pupils can visit throughout the year and experience seasonal food production first hand. Visit the website at **www.foodforlife.org.uk**

These farm visits are educating future consumers as well as their parents. A recent study by Kingston University found that 54% of parents said they had learned something from their child's farm visit, and that children's trips to farms influenced consumer behaviour. Sixteen per cent of parents said they would now be more prepared to make changes to their food choices, and buy more local, seasonal or organic products.

EDUCATION

SCHOOL DINNERS

JEANETTE ORREY WORKED AS A DINNER LADY FOR 20 YEARS AND PIONEERED FRESH, LOCAL AND ORGANIC FOOD IN SCHOOLS. HER ACHIEVEMENTS AND GUIDANCE LED TO THE SUCCESS OF THE FOOD FOR LIFE PARTNERSHIP CAMPAIGN AND INSPIRED JAMIE OLIVER'S FIGHT TO IMPROVE SCHOOL MEALS.

It all started when I was the catering manager at St Peter's Primary School in Nottinghamshire. I was employed by the Local Authority, which had introduced Thatcher's recommendations for 'best value' for school meals. In practice, 'best value' meant using the cheapest ingredients, taking away equipment and catering staff hours, and providing everything in boxes pre-prepared. Carrots, onions, potatoes came pre-prepared, the coleslaw came ready-shredded (and it had the most awful smell). I just couldn't believe that this was what we were serving to the children. None of the kitchen staff would eat it, including me. I knew something had to be done.

In 2000, with the head teacher's and governors' support we decided to take the catering in-house. To begin with it was very frightening as I knew I really had to make it work to prove that freshly prepared school food was the way forward. I started slowly by introducing local meat, then milk and then local and organic veg and potatoes. It was hard work in the beginning, but meal numbers increased and it turned into a huge success with pupils and parents. In my quest to find new suppliers, I realised that I could source local and organic produce directly from the growers at the same price as non-organic produce through a centralised wholesaler.

It's not rocket science feeding kids, really. I have three boys of my own who are all over 6ft and they take some feeding even now. I've always fed them and my husband home-cooked food made from scratch. What was important to me was that I could look the parents in the eye and tell them where the food

I was serving their children came from. I just wanted to serve good, wholesome, honest food and it went down a treat.

While we had changed the food at St Peter's, we never thought about the bigger picture.

It wasn't until I received a Soil Association award in 2002 and met Lizzie Vann (founder of Organix) that the real school food revolution began. It must be said that people had been campaigning for better school meals long before I came onto the scene, but I think we were just in the right place at the right time to make something happen.

Lizzie and I then decided that we needed to roll this out and support more schools to do what we did at St Peter's. We took our 'Food for Life' idea to the Soil Association and together we set up a six-school pilot scheme, which later led to the Food for Life Partnership.

Part and parcel of this pilot scheme was a 'whole school approach' to food, which includes what I call 'the dining experience'. Many children don't eat at a dining table at home and social skills are lost, so in my mind it's important they get this experience in school. Using real cutlery and crockery and having tablecloths on the tables makes the dining hall into a dining room, where they can sit down and have the time to enjoy their food and socialise. A good atmosphere makes the children appreciate the food more, and gradually, as this improves, schools feel they can invite parents and members of the local community in to have lunch with the children.

Food is so much more powerful than many of us realise and what happens in the school has a huge impact on the local community. Whether in the city or the countryside, trusting relationships can be created between the older and younger generations by having them enjoy a well-prepared school lunch together or share growing and cooking experiences at school clubs. We can all learn from each other and schools are the perfect places to make this happen.

Alongside improving school meals, it's very important to get schools cooking, growing and visiting farms, as one without the other doesn't work. Children need to know where the food they eat comes from in order to appreciate it.

I've asked children where potatoes come from and their answer was 'trees'. That worries me. St Peter's Primary School gets much of its produce from the local Gonalston Farm Shop, which also hosts visits to teach children how the sausages they eat at school are made, and to give them tastes of the local cheese and so on. The children then go home and talk about the food they tried there, which inspires parents to go down to the farm shop to taste and buy local food too.

It's the same with growing. If the children are allowed to grow vegetables and take it to the school cook, who uses it for school dinners, they will eat it. Never mind that the 20 carrots didn't really do 200 dinners, the younger children still believe that's the case and are so proud that the carrots they have grown are on the menu.

My hope for the future is that every child can sit down at school and enjoy a good, wholesome lunch knowing where it has come from and that the catering staff are given the recognition and status they deserve. These staff play a crucial role in improving the quality and provenance of school meals in this country and in educating children about food through what they serve them at school.

We are moving in the right direction, but we are going to be under a lot of pressure in the next few years with the government cutting costs and the rise in food and oil prices. We only have one shot at this and we have to get it right. We owe it to the future generations.

"*Food is so much more powerful than many of us realise and what happens in the school has a huge impact on the local community.*"

TRANSFORM THE FOOD CULTURE IN YOUR SCHOOL

PROVIDING BETTER SCHOOL DINNERS OR STARTING A SCHOOL GARDENING CLUB ARE GREAT ACTIONS ON THEIR OWN. DOING BOTH TOGETHER, ALONGSIDE COOKING LESSONS, FARM VISITS AND AN INTEGRATED APPROACH TO HEALTHY FOOD AND EATING, IS EVEN BETTER. DRIVING THIS CHANGE IN SCHOOLS IS EASIER THAN IT MIGHT AT FIRST SEEM.

The Food for Life Partnership provides a clear and effective framework for bringing these changes about. It also provides a bridge between schools and the wider community — when a school signs up to it everyone in the community can get involved, not just local parents.

GETTING STARTED

Schools are busy places, so the first challenge is to convince the teachers to sign up to the scheme. You can check if a school is already enrolled at **www.foodforlife.org.uk**

If the school is not already enrolled you will need to approach the head teacher and chair of governors and ask for a meeting to discuss joining the Food for Life Partnership. The scheme is broken down into three milestones: on fulfilling the criteria for each a school can qualify for a bronze, silver or gold award. So, before the meeting check the criteria and tick off the things you know the school is already doing. It would also help to find other schools involved in the local area, as pointing out real examples to head teachers is a great way of

selling the benefits of the scheme. It's also worth finding out if school meals are provided in-house or by a local authority or private caterer. If there is a caterer involved it will need to agree to support your school in changing menus — depending on the attitude of the caterer this may make things easier or more difficult.

CHILDREN OF THE REVOLUTION

Once a school is signed up to the Partnership it will need to develop a series of activities around eating, cooking and growing food to qualify for the three awards. For parents or community members there are many ways to help the school transform its food culture.

The first place to start is with the criteria for awards. Choose a goal that fits your skills or enthusiasm and offer to help the school work towards it. See if you can find other parents, or members of your local community, who are willing to get involved. There are a number of small 'hands-on' goals that you can help with, such as starting up a lunchtime or after-school gardening club, running a compost scheme for leftover fruit from snack time, or volunteering to demonstrate cooking techniques at the school cooking club.

If you have experience of running a café or restaurant your expertise could help the school improve its catering or dining experience. Often children are put off school meals by the length of the queues and the noisy environment, so helping to improve the dining experience can be crucial in encouraging uptake of healthier meals. A great way to share expertise is to volunteer to join the School Nutrition Action Group (SNAG). A SNAG is a school-based group in which teaching staff, pupils, parents and caterers work together to review and improve the school food service. It is at the heart of the Partnership's approach to food education, so if your school doesn't have one of these already, offer to set one up. If you have expertise you want to share but can't commit regular time, you can also share your experiences by offering to take an assembly.

PARENT POWER

A key goal of the Food for Life Partnership's programme is to amplify healthy food messages as far as possible. Children eat better food at school, are taught about the production of good, sustainable food and, hopefully, take these messages home to their parents. The easiest way of keeping parents informed and inspired in the school's activity is through the school newsletter.

Engaging the school's Parent Teacher Association (PTA) in the programme can also be helpful. The PTA organises many activities, such as school fairs, which can be used to raise the profile of the work that teachers, pupils and parents are doing on food. It can also help if the school wants to influence outside agencies such as a local authority or catering company. An organised letter writing campaign involving as many parents as possible is a very effective way of getting local councillors, school governors or the local paper to take notice.

WHO'S WHO AT SCHOOL

The head teacher is the first person to talk to about joining the Food for Life Partnership. Once a school has signed up, however, there are many more figures crucial to the scheme's success. These include:

SCHOOL COOK OR CATERING MANAGER

Employed directly by the school, a private catering company or the local authority, school cooks hold the key to transforming the quality of school meals and need the support of the school and caterer to make changes happen.

SITE MANAGER

The site manager, or caretaker, has responsibility for the building, the grounds and waste management, including any composting projects or gardening plans.

SCHOOL COUNCIL

The head teacher can ask the school council to discuss the Food for Life Partnership programme and provide support and ideas.

PSHE COORDINATOR

All children study Personal, Social and Health Education (PSHE). Talk to the co-ordinator about the Food for Life Partnership and let them know that there are teaching resources available on the website.

SCHOOL GOVERNORS

Ask if the governors will consider appointing one of themselves to take responsibility for school meals and food education. Invite them into the school for lunch.

CALL TO ACTION

ACT NOW

- Join your child for a school lunch – find out what the dining experience is really like.

- Ask about the provenance of the meat your local school serves.

- Offer to start a compost scheme for your school from leftover snack-time fruit.

- Ask your local head teacher to consider joining the Food for Life Partnership scheme.

ACT TOGETHER

- Talk to the PTA about how and why the school's food culture should improve.

- Use the school newsletter to tell parents about children's food education.

- Suggest a skills audit – parents could be cooks, farmers, gardeners or health professionals and might be happy to share their experience if they think it's helpful.

ACT DIFFERENTLY

- Offer to set up a school gardening or cooking club.

- Show and tell – if you have some expertise, offer to share it with children at a school assembly.

- Get writing – if your school's food is locked into a local authority caterer then write to local papers and councillors to call for systemic change at a district or county level.

"ARE YOU ENJOYING YOUR MEAL, MISS?"

asks the 10-year-old Happy Lunchtime Helper. The only possible reply is, yes, it's delicious. The lasagne has been cooked from scratch and is served with salad, beetroot and carrots from the school garden. There are tablecloths on all the tables in the dining hall – aka 'The Purple Planet' – and relaxing music flows from the big speakers on the walls.

In meeting the Food for Life Partnership Gold criteria, St John's has worked closely with Bath and North East Somerset Council catering, who provide food for the school. Its meals are now at least 75% freshly prepared, 50% local and 30% organic, and the majority of pupils are choosing to eat them. The school has also instigated farm visits, organised growing activities in school and ensured that every pupil has at least 12 hours of practical cooking each year.

The growing aspect of the programme has been particularly popular. The school has put up a polytunnel to help the children understand the whole cycle of growing organic food from seed to harvest. The interest has been infectious; since the project began more and more parents have signed up for allotments.

Perhaps the most impressive change is the dining experience. The Happy Lunchtime Helpers are pupils from Years 5 and 6 who serve water and dessert, police the 'no shouting and running rule' and ensure that younger children are happy. This role was introduced after pupils' responses to a survey showed their desire for a nicer dining hall alongside happy supervisors – not grumpy grown-up ones. 'We didn't realise the children didn't like the hustle and bustle at lunchtime,' says head teacher Carolyn Banfield.

Summing up the impact on the school, Carolyn continues: 'Our achievements over the past two years have exceeded all expectations. By bringing together aspects related to food culture, providing opportunities to visit local farms and implementing cookery and growing experiences within the curriculum, we have been able to influence pupil and parent understanding of healthy lifestyles, sustainability and the positive impact we can have on our local and worldwide environment. The benefits to the children have been significant, encouraging them to become discerning and well-informed individuals.'

111

05
CITY FOOD

CITIES ARE RICH ECOSYSTEMS THAT REFLECT THE CULTURE
AND THE VALUES OF THE PEOPLE WHO LIVE IN THEM.
THEY CAN BE BARREN, WASTEFUL AND POLLUTING OR THEY
CAN BE BOUNTIFUL, SUSTAINABLE AND SUPPORTIVE. IF WE
WANT A FUTURE WHERE OUR CITIES PULL THEIR WEIGHT
ENVIRONMENTALLY WE NEED TO START NOW.

IN 2008 MORE THAN HALF THE WORLD'S POPULATION OFFICIALLY BECAME CITY DWELLERS. THIS MASS URBAN MIGRATION IS ONGOING. BY 2050 IT IS ESTIMATED THAT UP TO 80% OF US WILL LIVE IN CITIES. A GLOBAL CHANGE OF LIFESTYLE ON THIS SCALE HAS IMPORTANT IMPLICATIONS FOR SUSTAINABILITY AND FOOD CULTURE, ESPECIALLY AS MORE MEGA-CITIES DEVELOP WITH POPULATIONS OVER 10 MILLION.

Cities can be an efficient use of land, housing many more people per acre than in the countryside. Daily journeys in a city are likely to be shorter and, theoretically, more energy efficient. In reality, though, cities place a heavy burden on the environment. They cover only about 2% of the earth's surface but they consume three-quarters of its resources and produce three-quarters of its waste. It is estimated, for example, that a city the size of London needs roughly 58 times its land area to supply its residents with food and timber.

So we need to ask ourselves: What are cities? Why do we live in them? What notions of urban life have we inherited that no longer work today and might endanger our future? How do we need to change?

Most people live in cities because they are convenient. They meet our needs for food, shelter and employment seemingly effortlessly. Entertainment is laid on, public transport runs continually and food arrives on the shelves as if by magic. But this easy lifestyle is fuelled by oil. It will have to change, along with our mindsets, as the reality of climate change and peak oil begins to bite. The cities of the future will need to pull their weight environmentally, to give back rather than just consume.

Since the Second World War our cities have been surrounded by large parcels of agricultural land providing food within a short distance of the city centre. But as cities have spread outwards with the rising demand for housing and the development of industrial sites, this open land has been eroded. This has coincided with the growth of the globalised food network, and as a result the food for our cities now comes from further and further away.

So how do we change our cities to make them more resourceful and responsive to environmental needs? It's easy to feel helpless in the face of this challenge, but remember that cities are made up of people with attitudes, passions and values. We can draw on these to create a new, sustainable urban environment.

Food solutions currently taking hold in cities are imaginative, complex and diverse. The concentration of creative ideas that arises from having so many people in one space has led to ingenious ideas and to a willingness to use any available plot, verge, canal bank, building site or balcony to help sustain a steady supply of food for our families.

City farms, market gardens, farmers' markets all maintain a vital link between the city and the wider rural environment. They provide opportunities for children to learn, for the unemployed to find meaningful work and acquire new skills, for people who might otherwise feel marginalised to feel part of a thriving local community.

Growing your own on balconies, rooftops and windowsills supports a vital and unique green corridor through the city for wildlife.

The needs of urban dwellers can also fuel innovative social enterprises and food distribution systems, such as urban farms like Hackney's Growing Communities (see page 92) where people work together to provide food for the local area, or schemes to spread the bounty around by trading, or even giving away, surpluses from urban farms.

Nurturing sustainability and biodiversity in cities rebuilds a lost connection to the living world and fosters a sense of working together for a common good. This in turn can lead to feelings of responsibility, respect and care for the local environment and for each other.

"I THINK WE'D BE VERY FOOLISH TO EXPECT THAT WE CAN JUST IMPORT EVERYTHING FROM SOMEWHERE ELSE AND IMAGINE THAT THAT'S GOING TO LAST FOR EVER AND EVER AND EVER."

**HRH THE PRINCE OF WALES
BBC INTERVIEW OCTOBER 2005**

FEEDING THE CITY

DO YOU LIVE IN AN URBAN FOOD DESERT?

GROWING SOME OF YOUR OWN FOOD IS ONE WAY TO HOLD THE 'URBAN FOOD DESERT' AT BAY. AN URBAN FOOD DESERT IS WHERE RESIDENTS HAVE LITTLE OR NO ACCESS TO FRESH, HEALTHY PRODUCE AND ARE SURROUNDED BY SHOPS THAT STOCK A HIGH DEGREE OF FAST FOOD OR CONVENIENCE FOODS. AS CITIES HAVE EXPANDED OUTWARDS AND SUPERMARKETS HAVE REPLACED LOCAL GREENGROCERS, BUTCHERS AND BAKERIES, FOOD DESERTS IN INNER-CITY AREAS ARE BECOMING MORE COMMON. OFTEN RESIDENTS IN THESE AREAS HAVE INCOMES BELOW THE NATIONAL AVERAGE, BUT THEY HAVE TO PAY ALMOST DOUBLE THE PRICE FOR THEIR FOOD.

Urban food deserts impact on communities in unexpected ways. There is now a growing body of research that links poor diets with higher levels of violent and criminal behaviour. Bringing better food into your area may therefore have the unplanned benefits of making communities more peaceful places to live, as well as creating more work opportunities locally and greening up areas that might otherwise be a monotonous landscape of concrete and steel.

With a little vision and effort nothing is impossible – as the residents of Middlesborough have recently found out. In 2008 around 1,000 people in this city grew produce in window boxes, on balconies, roundabouts and even skips. Crops were planted in June and harvested in September, when they were cooked for the 'Meal for Middlesborough', eaten by 2,500 local residents. The local council has now given its support to the project and there are more than 280 growing sites across the city. Participants even receive recognised qualifications in urban growing, ensuring that more people have the skills necessary to meet future energy, climate and food challenges.

There are now around 1,000 community gardens in Britain. Another 200 city farms and community gardens are being developed. Across the country more and more schools are serving up meals made from fresh local ingredients, and even growing some of their own (see Chapter 4). In the process they are helping children gain a valuable understanding of where their food comes from. Some housing estates have land where residents can set up allotments or put their household waste to good use to make compost. If you are a keen gardener, share your know-how with neighbours. Start a club and share tools and talent to bring food-growing to the windowsills, balconies and rooftops. Planting vegetables in containers, setting up a market garden or organising a farmers' market in a local school can make a lasting contribution to a healthy community.

DON'T KNOW WHERE TO START?

Residents in south London who want to learn how to grow their own produce can benefit from the advice of groups like Food Up Front (www.foodupfront.org). For a small fee, members are provided with a 'starter kit' that includes a container, locally produced, peat-free compost and a choice of organic salad and herb seeds. They are given advice about how to use their front gardens, balconies, windowsills or back gardens to grow food with a high nutritional value and an extremely low cost. At the same time they are increasing the amount of vegetation in the urban environment. If you love growing food, why not start your own local support group to help others get growing?

GUERRILLA ALLOTMENTS AND GREEN ROOFTOPS

GUERRILLA GARDENERS ARE ACTIVIST GARDENERS WHO HELP BEAUTIFY LOCAL AREAS BY RENOVATING NEGLECTED PARCELS OF LAND – ANYTHING FROM VERGES TO ROUNDABOUTS TO ABANDONED SITES. OFTEN THEY WORK UNDER COVER OF DARKNESS HOEING, PLANTING AND NURTURING A BIT OF LAND BACK INTO LIFE. MOST GUERRILLA GARDENING FOCUSES AROUND ORNAMENTAL PLANTS, BUT SOME INVOLVES FOOD PRODUCTION. THESE GUERRILLA ALLOTMENTS CAN SPRING UP ON BUILDING SITES ALMOST OVERNIGHT AS THE GARDENERS USE GROW BAGS TO PRODUCE FRESH VEGETABLES.

Britain currently has around 74,000 acres of vacant or derelict brownfield land and other unused public spaces that – provided they are not contaminated by industrial pollutants – could easily play host to these temporary allotments. It's a practice that has worked in other cities. In New York some community gardens have moved from one site to another for more than 30 years. This 'land in limbo' can be put to good use and the portability of a guerrilla allotment means that if and when developers do move in the site can simply be taken elsewhere.

But there's more to greening the city landscape than ground-level gardens. Cities are ideal places for rooftop gardens. While it's not unusual to use rooftops to grow flowers and shrubs, these spaces can also be used to create mini urban farms that can provide food, improve biodiversity by creating a safe haven and a green corridor for insects and birds, and reduce the ecological footprint of the city.

Rooftop gardens can make cities more pleasant places to live. Buildings with roof gardens tend to be quieter inside, and can be much cooler in summer and warmer in winter. The more rooftop gardens we have the more we help fight the urban 'heat island' effect – the extreme temperature rises that the concrete and steel of the city help to foster. Gardens can help cool the city, then, as well as clean its air.

Rooftop gardens can also cut down on rainwater drainage. The soil absorbs the rain, which is sucked up by the plants and expired back into the atmosphere. Having roofs covered in plants transforms the grey, unproductive landscape of the city into a colourful, fertile and productive space.

WHAT CAN

TOMATOES LETTUCES AUBERGINES COURGETTES SWEET PEPPERS

YOU GROW

GREEN BEANS MELONS BOK CHOI ENDIVE ROCKET PARSLEY

IN A GROW

BASIL TARRAGON SPRING ONIONS RADISHES STUNTED CARROTS

BAG?

CUCUMBERS STRAWBERRIES

Grow bags are useful portable garden containers, but make sure you choose peat-free and organic. You can use them flat or stand them on their end, or even hang them up depending on what crop you want to grow. You can plant two to three different plants in a bag measuring 35cm x 95cm. Plant in spring and you will have enough to provide you with several meals over the summer. Plants that do not have deep roots are most suitable. For plants with deeper roots try turning old tyres or building material sacks into useful containers.

AN URBAN HARVEST

FRUIT TREES ARE NOT THE PRESERVE OF PRIVATE GARDENS. IN CITIES ALL OVER THE UK THERE ARE FRUIT TREES GROWING ON PUBLIC LAND, IN PARKS AND CAR PARKS, ALONG STREETS AND CYCLE PATHS, IN SCHOOLS AND CHURCHYARDS. SOME ARE IN PEOPLE'S GARDENS, BUT NEVER GET USED. OFTEN THE FRUIT GOES UNPICKED AND UNAPPRECIATED AND IS EVENTUALLY WASTED.

It's hard to imagine cities as orchards when we are so used to buying fruit in neat plastic bags and boxes from places like Spain, South Africa and Chile. But literally tonnes of fruit grows right on our doorsteps including apples, pears, figs, plums, crab apples, blackberries, mulberries, strawberries and more. Many local councils have begun to cut down old fruit trees in the city, worried that the fruit will drop on cars and cause damage, or that it will fall to the pavement and cause a health and safety risk.

There is a better alternative. Initiatives across the globe, such as Fruit City in London and Fallen Fruit in Los Angeles, are mapping fruit trees across the urban space so more of us can enjoy them. Local 'scrumping' projects have sprung up to make use of city apples that would otherwise go to waste. In 2008 one project in north-east London picked nearly three tonnes of otherwise abandoned fruit.

Why not join an urban Abundance Group to help harvest this bounty and give it to those who need it most. The abundance movement started in Sheffield and has spread to Manchester, Bristol, Edinburgh, Nottingham, Leeds and Brixton in London. The fruit is pressed into juice or made into jams and pickles or sold loose at reduced rates to local families who otherwise would not have access to fresh fruit. Many of the varieties of fruit found in our cities are old, which makes a crucial contribution to biodiversity.

Don't let your local council cut down valuable fruit trees. Get them to follow the example of Manchester City Council, which recently committed £200,000 to plant thousands of fruit and nut trees and vegetable patches in each of the city's 135 parks, with an invitation to 'help yourself'. The scheme also involves planting 20,000 strawberry, raspberry and soft fruit bushes around the city, setting up beehives in a dozen parks and allotments, and planting free herbs such as mint and parsley in every park. Every city should be doing this so get involved and get lobbying.

For more information, visit Sheffield Abundance Group's website at: **www.growsheffield.com/pages/ groShefAbund.html**

CITY HONEY

Amazingly, the majority of the UK's private beekeepers are in cities. If your roof or balcony has a good open approach and is not too high up, you could keep a small hive to produce your own honey and help boost declining honeybee numbers. City bees often tend to be healthier than those in the countryside because there is a wider diversity of plants available for food, and less exposure to agricultural chemicals and pesticides.

Maintaining many small hives can also be a more resilient way of beekeeping than maintaining a few large ones, where one disease can potentially wipe out several colonies at once (see page 63). You can now buy a specially made 'urban beehive' known as the Beehaus (available from www.omlet.co.uk), which is perfectly suited to the city environment. For useful advice on sustainable beekeeping, log on to www.biobees.com

Keeping bees is increasing in popularity. The British Beekeepers' Association (BBKA) reporting a 25% jump in membership in 2009. Honey produced in urban areas can be surprisingly tasty and rich, as city bees have a much greater diversity of plants from which to collect pollen. If you want to learn more the BBKA runs courses on beekeeping to help get you started.

THE UK IS HOME TO ABOUT 60 CITY FARMS, MANY IN BUILT-UP, SOCIALLY DEPRIVED AREAS WHERE WASTE LAND HAS BEEN RECLAIMED, CREATING MUCH NEEDED OPEN, GREEN SPACES. EACH FARM IS UNIQUE AND MANY ARE RUN AS SOCIAL ENTERPRISES BY A COMMUNITY GROUP OR LOCAL AUTHORITY.

A typical city farm has a variety of teaching rooms, gardens, growing plots and sometimes cafés. They usually have a range of animals including pigs, sheep, goats, chickens, geese, cows, donkeys, ponies and bees. Many city farms act as important preserves of rare breeds of livestock.

Mudchute Park and Farm pictured here is the largest city farm in London with 32 acres of countryside in the middle of the Isle of Dogs to share with friendly fur and feathered creatures. The farm runs community events, hosts community groups or just simply provides a great place for a family picnic.

SUPPORT YOUR CITY FARM

The primary purpose of city farms is to give people a chance to see agriculture in action. They have an especially important role to play in teaching urban children where their food comes from, how important farming is and how much fun growing food can be. On a typical visit, children are allowed to get close to animals, perhaps pick up some newly laid eggs or even learn how to milk a goat. Although producing food is not the main purpose of a city farm, many do produce fruit, vegetables, milk, eggs, honey and dairy products for selling to local residents.

City farms are charities and rely heavily on volunteers. They allow members of the public in for free or for a small charge. We need to value our city farms and help them thrive. If you have a few hours to spare why not volunteer? There are no restrictions on who can help and people from all backgrounds are welcomed. An estimated 500,000 people currently volunteer on city farms and they attract over three million visitors each year.

Volunteering at a city farm gives you a chance to be 'hands-on' in a variety of agricultural tasks, from mucking out stables and pens, to general farm maintenance, to feeding and looking after the animals. You can work in a dairy or look after the beehives or tend the vegetable patch, depending on your interests and where help is needed. Or you can help with educational activities, teaching school children about food production. The Federation of City Farms can tell you more about how to get involved see **www.farmgarden.org.uk**.

PROTECTING THE FOODSHED

CHANCES ARE THAT THE FOOD YOU ARE EATING TODAY IS 'JUST-IN-TIME' FOOD. IT CERTAINLY WILL BE IF YOU BOUGHT IT AT A SUPERMARKET. OUR SUPERMARKET FOOD SYSTEM RELIES ON WHAT ARE CALLED 'JUST-IN-TIME' DELIVERIES THAT ARRIVE JUST BEFORE THE STORE RUNS OUT OF STOCK.

It may make sense for profit flow but it makes very little sense in the bigger picture of food security. It is estimated that if oil ran out tomorrow our cities would be three days away from running completely out of food. This is inherently unstable and requires a radical rethink of our national foodshed.

The foodshed refers to our national store cupboard. It encompasses everything from plough to plate: the land used to produce the food, the routes it travels to get to us, the markets it goes through and the tables it ends up on. For most cities the foodshed is the entire world — an impractical system that is rather like keeping the ingredients for your evening meal at a friend's house 50 miles away. In this global model, food can often travel back and forth thousands of miles to different processing plants before it eventually reaches you.

The Soil Association has calculated staggering figures for the number of food miles accumulated by many of our everyday foods in the UK. The CO_2 emissions from moving all this food around the planet is a direct contributor to the catastrophic problem of global warming (see page 165).

The term foodshed was originally coined to describe the flow of food around the world. More recently, though, it has come to mean food produced on a local or regional scale. Making use of land closer to the city centre is an important part of securing the foodshed. While no one would argue that cities can be totally self-sufficient they can become more so by making better use of the peri-urban greenbelt and of common land. Much of this productive land is currently under threat from government plans to build more housing.

A useful model for the urban foodshed has been devised by Growing Communities (**www.growingcommunities.org**), a market garden project in Hackney in London, which produces 450 vegetable boxes a week for an inner-city area as well as supplying and hosting a weekly farmers' market. Growing Communities suggests that by thinking locally and putting the necessary support systems in place the foodshed for a city like London would look something like this:

- 2.5% grown in the local borough
- 5% grown in the city itself – this includes salad greens and fruit, with boroughs trading their surplus city wide
- 17.5% from the peri-urban greenbelt – fruit, vegetables and produce grown on a larger scale such as carrots, lettuces, onions, leeks and brassicas
- 35% from the rural hinterlands within 100 miles of the city centre – field-scale produce and some arable livestock
- 20% from elsewhere in the UK – for instance arable livestock and larger field-scale production
- 20% from the rest of the world – spices, tea, chocolate etc.

Such schemes can work on both a small and large scale. In Manchester, the Unicorn Grocery (**www.unicorn-grocery.co.uk**) is a food co-op that sells a wide range of fresh, dried and processed food and drink, much of it organic and with a focus on local sourcing and fair trade. It also sells household, bodycare and general grocery items. Unicorn is founded on ethical and environmental business principles and much of its produce comes from the peri-urban greenbelt in nearby Cheshire. Keeping prices in line with the supermarkets, the co-op is one of the largest independent wholefood groceries in the UK today and has an annual turnover of around £3.5 million.

The Better Food Company in Bristol (**www.betterfood.co.uk**) is an organic supermarket, also founded on ethical and sustainable business practices, that sources much of its produce from its own market garden 10 miles away from the store.

To achieve a higher level of urban self-sufficiency businesses and consumers need to think differently about what they eat and how they shop. For farmers and other food producers to feel confident about opting into local markets, rather than chasing the global food train, they need to know that there is a home market ready for their goods. Farmers' markets and organic box schemes help create this market – which is why they need our support.

Government could also be doing so much more to encourage a secure foodshed. It could require hospitals, schools and other public sector institutions to purchase a significant amount of their produce from local producers and UK farmers. Currently only 2% of government-procured food is sourced locally.

Each year the UK government spends £1.8 billion on the procurement of food for schools, hospitals and prisons. Imagine what this investment could do if it were directed at local farmers and producers. If just 20% of it went on local food procurement it would represent an investment of £320 million in fresh local organic food for some of the most vulnerable members of the population.

In fact there is already a model for authorities to do this – public sector institutions can work towards the Soil Association's Food for Life Catering Mark, which ensures that fresh, local and organic food is served. For more information on the Catering Mark, see **www. soilassociation.org/catering.aspx** and **www.foodforlife.org**

COWS ON THE COMMONS

From the coast and lowlands to the vast upland and hill areas, the UK is home to 8,765 commons, accounting for nearly 1.4 million acres. This is privately owned land to which the general public has certain rights of access including the grazing of livestock. Much of the UK's common land is highly suitable for grazing cows and sheep, and pastoral farmers have been using it this way for centuries.

Encouraging the grazing of more common land could help small-scale livestock production. It would also be good for the environment: grazing helps maintain the landscape and absorb carbon, locking it into the soil through the grass. Possibilities definitely exist for increasing grazing on common land, but more government support is needed.

Bristol City Council, for example, is investigating the possibility of grazing organic beef cattle on Stoke Park – an 18th century parkland owned by the Council. The scheme could produce 6.5 tonnes of beef each year, which would supply local schools directly and local residents through a box scheme. Any surplus will be sold at Bristol's farmers' market or to the Bristol restaurant trade. Meanwhile, residents in Cambridge are lobbying to restore Midsummer Common (**http://www.midsummercommon.org.uk**) to make more space for the grazing of livestock. If these schemes are successful they could be replicated all around the country – especially if voters start encouraging it.

CALL TO ACTION

ACT NOW

- Stop your local council cutting down fruit trees – encourage them to plant more instead.
- Make 80% of your diet UK produced – start by ordering a veg box from your local market garden, food co-op or CSA.
- Buy a grow bag and get growing.
- Turn your rooftop into a mini urban farm.

ACT TOGETHER

- Volunteer to help at a city farm.
- Get together with neighbours on your housing estate and start a compost heap.
- Have a street party to share food grown by your friends and neighbours.
- Help maintain a vegetable patch in a public space such as your local park.

ACT DIFFERENTLY

- Look at a building site and see a potential guerrilla allotment.
- Become an urban beekeeper.
- Help harvest city fruit.
- Start a city growing club or group and share tools, tips and talent.

RECIPE

5 PARTS POWDERED CLAY

1 PART PEAT-FREE COMPOST

1 PART WILDFLOWER SEED MIX

DIY SEED BOMB

SEED BOMBS ARE A SIMPLE, ANONYMOUS, LOW-MAINTENANCE WAY OF GREENING UP AN OTHERWISE DISUSED AREA OF LAND. BOMBARDING AN AREA WITH A DIY MIXTURE OF SEED AND CLAY CAN TURN BARREN SOIL INTO A RICH HAVEN FOR LOCAL WILDLIFE AND BRING MUCH NEEDED COLOUR TO NEGLECTED CORNERS OF OUR NEIGHBOURHOODS.

METHOD

Step 1: Mix up the seed mix with the compost — you can use any seeds you want, but native wildflowers fare best in our climate.

Step 2: Add the powdered clay and start to add a little water, a drop at a time, and mix. You want to add just enough water for the bomb to bind together, but not so much that it gets too wet or sludgy.

Step 3: Once you have a fairly stiff consistency, start kneading the clay mix into a firm ball — you want it to be robust enough that it won't break open once thrown.

Step 4: Leave the finished balls on a sunny windowsill for a day or two to dry off, and then you're ready to start seed bombing.

You want the bomb to survive the impact so the seeds remain surrounded by the compost and clay. The sun and rain will gradually break the bomb down and let in air — at which point the seed will be able to germinate.

Happy bombing...

A SHORT WORD
with Carolyn Steel

Architect, lecturer and author of
Hungry City: How Food Shapes Our Lives (2008)

SITOPIA: CITY FOOD

WE LIVE IN A WORLD SHAPED BY FOOD. OUR CITIES AND LANDSCAPES WERE FORGED BY IT. OUR DAILY ROUTINES REVOLVE AROUND IT. OUR SOCIAL EXCHANGES ARE TEMPERED BY IT. POLITICS AND ECONOMICS ARE DRIVEN BY IT. OUR ECOLOGICAL FOOTPRINT IS DOMINATED BY IT. OUR SENSE OF IDENTITY IS INSEPARABLE FROM IT. OUR SURVIVAL DEPENDS ON IT.

Why, then, have we in the West come to consider food as just another commodity — something to be made as cheap and convenient as possible, while we get on with the 'more important' things in life?

We take it for granted that if we walk into a restaurant or supermarket, food will be there, having arrived magically from somewhere else. Yet the systems and processes that allow us to be so careless with this, our most vital resource, are destroying the planet faster than any human activity in history. Food, agriculture and deforestation together account for one third of global GHG emissions. Nineteen million hectares of rainforest are lost every year to agriculture, while a similar quantity of existing farmland is lost to salinisation and erosion.

Every calorie of food we consume in the West takes an average of 10 to produce, yet, in the US, half of the food produced is thrown away. Seventy per cent of all freshwater on the planet is used for agriculture, but ancient aquifers are running dry. A billion people worldwide are overweight, while a further billion starve. Global food systems are unethical and unsustainable, yet they are the basis upon which modern urban life depends.

Our profound disconnection with food is symptomatic of a deep social malaise. Two centuries of fossil-fuelled urban development have severed us, mentally and physically, from the natural world that sustains us. Yet food remains our most powerful link with nature: a reminder, in the midst of our urban existence, of our deeper bond with land, sea and sky. Greater awareness of that connection could present us with a vital opportunity. If we could only learn to reconnect with food, we could harness its potential, not just to feed our bodies, but to shape our lives in a far more positive way. We could use food as a design tool to rethink how we dwell on earth.

My word for this approach is sitopia, or 'food-place' (from the ancient Greek *sitos*, food, and *topos*, place). Unlike utopia, sitopia actually exists; indeed, we already live in it, albeit in a very unsatisfactory way. But by becoming more conscious of food and its effects, we can change that for the better. We can use food as a lens to question, disentangle and reconfigure the fundamental relationships in our lives. Food is the great connector. Once we grasp that, we can use it to ask questions such as: What is a good life? What is a community? What makes us happy? Through food, we can address everything from resource depletion and poverty to obesity, inequality and climate change.

Today, the widely held assumption is that the global future is urban. Three billion people live in cities at the moment; three billion more are expected to join them by 2050. But what does that mean in real life? Our very concept of a city, inherited from a distant, predominantly rural past, assumes that the means of supporting urban life can be endlessly extracted from the natural world. For the past two hundred years, industrialisation has fuelled that assumption. The result has been an unprecedented explosion

of urban development, accompanied by the dangerous illusion that cities are independent, immaculate and unstoppable.

Now that the illusion is wearing off, we urgently need a new model – one that recognises the vital role that cities play in the global ecology. But how are we to arrive at finding such a model? Many clues lie in the past. Before industrialisation, the greatest problem cities faced was that of feeding themselves. Without the benefit of machinery, agrichemicals, refrigeration and rapid transport, cities were forced to be both frugal and inventive with their food supplies.

No city was built without first considering where its sustenance was to come from, and food miles were always kept to a minimum, with perishable foods such as fruit and vegetables produced as close by as possible. Fresh foods, including meat from grass-fed livestock, were consumed seasonally, with the excess preserved through salting, drying or pickling. Nothing was wasted: food scraps were fed to pigs, and human and animal waste was spread as fertiliser on the land.

Few would suggest a return to what was undoubtedly a tough and malodorous existence in the pre-industrial world, yet there is much we can learn from it. Limited by the constraints of geography, pre-industrial cities were forced to live within their means, something we must learn to do once more. Far from damaging our quality of

life, such a shift could, if handled intelligently, vastly improve it, along with the lives of all those around the world to whom we are intimately bound through food.

With the dual benefits of hindsight and technology, we have the unprecedented capacity to invent a way of life that balances the urban-rural relationship – the pivotal core of civilisation. Nothing short of a complete recalibration of that relationship is needed. We must create new social, political, economic, physical and cultural networks in order to make rural and urban life equally attractive and viable. We must forge new forms of dwelling that blend them together. We must, as Patrick Geddes wrote a hundred years ago, 'make the field gain on the street, not merely the street gain on the field'.

For the past two hundred years, we have suffered a collective amnesia about our place in the organic order. Now we must re-embrace it. What is needed is not so much a technological revolution as a mental one: a recognition that, despite the fact that we live in steel-and-concrete cities, we remain flesh-and-blood animals, with animal needs. Food's ability to transcend boundaries makes it the ideal collaborative, multidisciplinary tool. But more importantly, food represents our cultural values: our desire to be good, to find meaning in existence, to transcend mere survival. Such aspirations, after all, are what distinguish us from the merely animal, and make life on earth worth living.

Food represents our cultural values: our desire to be good, to find meaning in existence, to transcend mere survival.

06

FARM

FAR FROM BEING A RETREAT TO THE PAST, ORGANIC FARMING
IS A FORWARD-LOOKING SOLUTION THAT CAN HELP OUR
FARMERS BE MORE RESILIENT IN THE FACE OF CLIMATE
CHANGE AND PEAK OIL. IT'S THE BEST WAY TO ENSURE
A SECURE FOOD SUPPLY, CREATE MORE JOBS AND MAINTAIN
THE PRODUCTIVITY OF OUR LAND.

"ORGANIC AGRICULTURE ENABLES ECOSYSTEMS TO BETTER ADJUST TO THE EFFECTS OF CLIMATE CHANGE... [IT] PERFORMS BETTER THAN CONVENTIONAL AGRICULTURE... BOTH ON DIRECT ENERGY CONSUMPTION (FUEL AND OIL) AND INDIRECT CONSUMPTION (SYNTHETIC FERTILISERS AND PESTICIDES) WITH HIGH EFFICIENCY IN ENERGY USE."

UNITED NATIONS FOOD AND AGRICULTURAL ORGANIZATION, ORGANIC AGRICULTURE ENVIRONMENT AND FOOD SECURITY (2002).

TODAY, HOW WE GROW AND PRODUCE OUR FOOD SITS SQUARELY ON THE FRONTLINE OF ALL THE CHALLENGES WE FACE. OUR FARMERS ARE ALREADY FEELING THE EFFECTS OF HIGH OIL PRICES AND A CHANGING CLIMATE. IF WE ARE TO MEET THESE CHALLENGES OUR FARMING PRACTICES WILL NEED TO EVOLVE AND THRIVE IN TWO KEY WAYS. FIRST OUR FARMS HAVE TO BECOME PART OF A GLOBAL CLIMATE CHANGE SOLUTION, TO MITIGATE CLIMATE CHANGE BY REDUCING THE IMPACT OF AGRICULTURE. SECOND THEY HAVE TO ADAPT TO CHANGES ALREADY IN MOTION, SUCH AS THOSE IN GLOBAL WEATHER AND ITS EFFECTS ON LAND AND CROPS, IN ORDER TO MAINTAIN A STABLE FOOD SUPPLY.

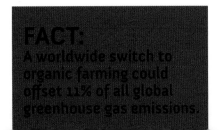

FACT:
A worldwide switch to organic farming could offset 11% of all global greenhouse gas emissions.

FARMING FOR THE FUTURE

Organic agriculture can help with both. In fact, it may be the single most important contributor to successful and bountiful farming in the future.

If it's hard to see how farming might play a role in saving the world from (self) destruction this may be, in part, because farming has become invisible to most of us over recent decades. Greater mechanisation has meant that fewer people are needed to work the land. Indeed, for more than half a century, governments and industry leaders have seen shedding labour as evidence of the greater efficiency of intensive agricultural. Consider what has happened in just a hundred years: in 1901, 30% of the UK's workforce was employed in land-related activities such as farming, forestry, horticulture, equestrianism and conservation; today, it is around 1%.

This means that many of us have never met a farmer, let alone sat down and talked to one about what life on the farm is really like. It was only as food prices began to rise in 2007–08 and food riots broke out across the world that many of us began to think about what farmers do, and to link what was happening globally with climate change and fossil fuel dependency back to our food system.

Likewise, if it's hard to see how organic farming might be the answer to these challenges it is because of a misconception of organic as a throwback to a 'charming' age before mechanisation. Farming has never been a 'charming' profession. It is the hard work that feeds the world and can be frustratingly dependent on the vagaries of geography and climate.

For example, where weather is concerned farmers have always expected the unexpected and are far more conscious of climatic conditions than most of us. But there are limits to what they can cope with while still producing enough food for everyone and making a decent living from their work. As climate change takes hold, farmers will be the first to feel the full force of new weather conditions such as sudden heatwaves, flash floods and prolonged storms.

To protect our farmers and ourselves we need a genuine transformation of our farming system that makes it responsive to today's challenges rather than leaving it trapped in yesterday's mistakes.

ORGANIC AGRICULTURE IS THE ANSWER

Much of this book is dedicated to individual action but the collective action of our farmers — today and tomorrow — can constitute a powerful collective response. This is, quite literally, activism from the ground up, and it can turn our world around, regenerate the land, restore our health and our faith in food, and keep our society resilient in the face of future challenges.

For our farmers to grasp this opportunity they need support. Given our escalating climate emergency, we all have a role to play in making sure organic agriculture grows and thrives. Government must provide incentives for encouraging farming practice and soil management that minimises carbon emissions and maximises carbon storage in agricultural soils.

As consumers we can help by including more fresh, organic produce in our diet, sourced from local suppliers. We can also refuse to support the introduction of genetically modified crops (see Chapter 7). These actions shift the demands of the market in favour of better farming and better food — a change that neither politicians nor producers can argue with.

IN CONTRAST TO THE CURRENT FARMING MODEL, ORGANIC AGRICULTURE REPRESENTS A DELIBERATE ATTEMPT TO MAKE THE BEST USE OF LOCAL AND NATURAL, AS WELL AS HUMAN AND SOCIAL, RESOURCES. FOR MOST ORGANIC FARMERS THE TERM 'ORGANIC' REPRESENTS A SYSTEM OF AGRICULTURE RATHER THAN A SET OF UNRELATED TECHNOLOGIES, WHICH SEEMS TO DOMINATE INDUSTRIAL FARMING.

Organic farming is defined as an approach that aims to create agricultural systems that are integrated, humane, and environmentally and economically sustainable. A 2002 Food and Agriculture Organization report describes it as representing a system in which the farm is 'an organism, in which the component parts – the soil minerals, organic matter, micro-organisms, insects, plants, animals and humans – interact to create a coherent and stable whole'.

It is the emphasis on stability and coherence that makes organic the best way to address some of our most pressing problems, both now and in the future.

FEWER CARBON EMISSIONS

Organic farming is our most effective short-term strategy for turning our soil back into an effective living carbon sink. Healthy soil stores carbon when organic matter is added to it and decomposed by soil microbial activity. This can work through the use of compost or animal manure; the use of 'green manures' or crops like clover; and the grazing

of permanent grassland with extensive root systems. New research by the Soil Association shows that organic farming practices produce 20% higher soil carbon levels than non-organic farming in Europe, North America and Australasia. In the UK, widespread adoption of organic farming practices would offset at least 23% of UK agricultural GHG emissions. Unlike other technologies, such as carbon capture and storage, it is something we can put into practice now, not in 50 years' time.

LESS ENERGY-INTENSIVE

Most of the energy inputs of intensive farming come from the use of pesticides and fertilisers. Organic's focus on 'soil not oil' means that if all farms in England and Wales switched to an organic production system – which relies on healthy soils to increase yields and fight pests – energy-intensive inputs to farming would fall dramatically; fertiliser inputs would be cut by 95% and pesticide sprays by 98%.

LESS POLLUTION

Using fewer chemical fertilisers also reduces run-off, which can pollute ponds, streams, lakes, rivers, aquifers, estuaries and seas. This run-off causes an effect called eutrophication, where algal blooms starve the waterways of oxygen, killing all aquatic wildlife. By avoiding the use of pesticides, organic farming also ensures that the food it produces is not contaminated by these chemicals.

HEALTHIER SOIL

Organic methods reduce soil erosion while improving soil quality. Not only do healthier soils fix nitrogen (the stuff that helps plants grow) more efficiently, and therefore support a greater level of biodiversity, they also act as efficient carbon sinks, removing CO_2 from the atmosphere.

INCREASED BIODIVERSITY

The symbiotic nature of organic farming with the natural world means that not only does organic farming protect wildlife and help it thrive, it also depends on that diversity to produce sustainable yields. Crop friendly insects, animals and companion plants can help increase yields by doing the job of synthetic pesticides.

EFFICIENT USE OF WATER

Healthy organic soils retain and release water more effectively, making farming less water intensive and reducing the impacts of flooding, droughts, water shortages and desertification – all of which will be crucial as we adapt to climate change.

BETTER ANIMAL WELFARE

Organic animals have to be free range and allowed to graze herbage and live a more natural life. Organic standards emphasise positive health – where the animal's immune system can easily overcome everyday disease challenges – rather than the control of disease. For example, the routine use of preventative antibiotics is prohibited. By raising fewer but more well-treated animals we can free up large quantities of grain for human consumption.

IMPROVED WORKER WELFARE

Pesticide exposure has been linked with a range of diseases including cancer and illnesses of the nervous system. These are generally more common amongst industrial farmers. In organic agriculture avoidance of pesticides protects the health and well-being of farm workers.

MORE JOBS IN RURAL COMMUNITIES

Organic farming is more labour intensive than conventional farming. The Soil Association estimates that turning our farms over to organic agriculture could see a 73% increase in farm jobs in the UK.

WORKS

MORE FROM LESS

THERE ARE CRITICS WHO CAST DOUBT OVER THE NOTION THAT ORGANIC CAN FEED THE WORLD AS WELL AS INTENSIVE FARMING. BUT THE FACT IS THAT THE CURRENT FOOD SYSTEM DOESN'T FEED THE WORLD. THERE ARE ONE BILLION PEOPLE (ABOUT 15% OF THE WORLD'S POPULATION) WHO ARE STARVING, WHILE AT THE SAME TIME, ACCORDING TO THE WASTE AND RESOURCES ACTION PROGRAMME (WRAP), AS MUCH AS 25% OF OUR FOOD IS THROWN AWAY BY CONSUMERS.

Even this doesn't begin to show the extent of the inequity since richer countries eat – and waste – much more than their fair share of the world's food supply.

WE NEED ANOTHER WAY

In every agricultural system there are losses and gains. The promise of the so-called Green Revolution of the 1960s – almost immediate higher yields through the use of fertilisers and pesticides – left many of us unconcerned about the longer term downsides.

Fifty years on we know that this particular revolution has led to a high dependence on fossil fuels and water, little return of organic matter to the earth and the erosion of topsoil. The greater mechanisation that came with the green revolution also led to the erosion of jobs in farming. And in spite of those higher yields, it has summarily failed to 'feed the world'.

The experience of the last half century has also taught us that the notion of yield is complex (see Chapter 7). If you judge the success or failure of a system based on a snapshot measurement of how much of a single product was grown per hectare of land at a particular point of time, this misses many important points about long-term sustainability. For example, green revolution cereals, bred to have less 'waste' straw and more fruit seemed a good idea because they promised higher yields. But less straw means less organic matter returned to the soil. Repeat this cycle over decades and you have large-scale soil erosion and a decline in overall yields.

ORGANIC FARMING ALSO COMES WITH LOSSES AND GAINS

In poorer countries, where, for a variety of reasons, the soil may not be as productive but the need for food is most urgent, there can be significant increases in yields. This means that in places where farmers can least afford to pay for expensive synthetic fertilisers and pesticides organic can succeed where the global food market has failed: that is, in getting food to where it is needed most.

In the developed world the picture is more complicated. Organic agriculture can see yield gains in some crops but losses in others.

Where gains are largest appear to be on smaller scale farms where manures, composts and wastes are more easily reapplied to the soil, and where crops are grown in rotation or together with other species. This highlights the need to look at farming in a more holistic way.

In 2008 the International Assessment of Agricultural Science and Technology for Development (IAASTD) published a groundbreaking report, based on a collaboration of more than 400 scientists, 30 governments from developed and developing countries, and 30 civil society organisations. It noted that, 'Historically, the path of global agricultural development has been narrowly focused on increased productivity rather than on a more holistic integration of natural resource management with food and nutritional security. A holistic, or systems-oriented, approach is preferable because it can address the difficult issues associated with the complexity of food and other production systems in different ecologies, locations and cultures.'

In conjunction with a change in diet, the will to cut down on waste, and more equitable trade laws, organic can indeed feed the world. A good starting point would be to see organic as a basic right for everyone, not as a luxury for the few.

LESS MEAT = LESS HEAT

One of the consequences of the Green Revolution – which brought with it the copious application of fertilisers and pesticides to increase crop yields – was a huge grain surplus. As a result, more than half the world's cereal crops today are fed to animals.

Across the globe this has led to a huge intensification of chicken and pig production, with large numbers of animals kept indoors in highly controlled environments. Feeding grain to ruminants such as cattle has also become the norm in the United States. Mounting evidence suggests that these products are less healthy and have a greater environmental impact than the meat and dairy produced from animals grazing in pastures.

For example, pastured animals produce meat that is higher in healthy essential fats, while those reared on grains produce meat that is higher in saturated fats. As our meat consumption has quadrupled in the past 50 years, this altered profile of fats in meat is believed to be a significant contributor to higher rates of obesity and heart disease.

But producing less meat is also important for tackling climate change. Dr Rajendra Pachauri, Chair of the Intergovernmental Panel on Climate Change, was one of the first major public figures to go on record saying that we need to eat less meat to help tackle climate change. Since then, many other influential figures have followed his lead.

Both problems – rising ill health and climate change – could be tackled by switching to a form of livestock production in which animals are reared to organic standards and fed mainly on grass. This would lead naturally to the production of less, but higher quality, meat. Simon Fairlie, editor of the influential *Land* journal, estimates that in the UK, given available land, we could still be rearing enough sustainably produced livestock to eat 250g of meat and just under 4kg of dairy produce per person each week. This is considerably more than we were eating in, say, 1945. We would make this change knowing that we were eating meat that enhanced rather than detracted from our health, the land and the atmosphere.

WHAT WE EAT AND HOW WE EAT SAYS A LOT ABOUT WHO WE ARE

A NATIONAL HEALTH SERVICE

IN 1943 LADY EVE BALFOUR, FOUNDER OF THE SOIL ASSOCIATION AND AUTHOR OF *THE LIVING SOIL*, SAW AGRICULTURE AS A VITAL SERVICE FOR THE NATION: 'IF THE NATION'S HEALTH DEPENDS ON THE WAY ITS FOOD IS GROWN, THEN AGRICULTURE MUST BE LOOKED UPON AS ONE OF THE HEALTH SERVICES, IN FACT THE PRIMARY HEALTH SERVICE.'

At the moment the National Health Service is groaning under the strain of treating preventable diseases, many of which are linked to the excess of sugar, meat and additives in our diets. The cost to the NHS of diet-related ill health is around £7 billion per year. Soil Association organic standards prohibit the use of hydrogenated fat and 313 additives approved by the government.

Eating is a primal, physical act but it is also a moral one. It reflects who we are – our character, our values and our ethics. Today the need to examine the values that we associate with the production and consumption of food is ever more urgent. For most of society those values can be summed up in three words: quick, cheap and convenient.

These values have led to a farming system that is destroying the planet. In his book *Fast Food Nation*, Eric Schlosser paints a devastating picture of how fast food has lured us into choosing diets deficient in nearly everything except calories, into supporting practices designed to deceive the consumer at every level and into accepting global systems that degrade most people and things involved in the process.

What we eat is also a political act. It affects not only how our food is produced, processed and distributed, but also who benefits, who pays and how animals, people and the earth are treated in the process.

SPREADING DISEASE

Intensive livestock practices lead to the unethical treatment of animals. But they also have important implications for human health. Crowding animals together increases the likely spread of disease. To combat this farmers routinely give animals antibiotics. This overuse of antibiotics has led to antibiotic resistance in bacteria. Studies also show that antibiotic residues can persist in foods made from these livestock, which potentially adds to antibiotic resistance in humans.

On a global scale intensive farming is responsible for the spread of diseases such as avian flu and swine flu. The practice of feeding animal products to cattle has been linked to mad cow disease in cattle and CJD in humans. Likewise, the spread of foot and mouth disease is more likely in an intensive setting: the resulting culls of affected livestock are a devastating blow to farmers and the food supply.

Organic standards avoid antibiotics as well as the kind of heavy stocking densities that can lead to the spread of these diseases.

THE FOOD SYSTEM THAT MEETS THE EXPECTATIONS OF A NEW FOOD CULTURE WILL NEED TO BE DRAMATICALLY DIFFERENT FROM TODAY'S INTENSIVE AND INDUSTRIALISED FOOD SYSTEM. MOST LIKELY IT WILL BE A NETWORK OF LOCAL, INTERDEPENDENT COMMUNITY FOOD SYSTEMS, MANY OF WHICH WILL BE WHOLLY OR PARTLY INDEPENDENT FROM THE GLOBAL SUPPLY CHAINS THAT ARE SO COMMON TODAY. IN ESSENCE IT WILL BE A SYSTEM THAT IS BASED ON RELATIONSHIPS AND A SENSE OF PERSONAL CONNECTEDNESS – TO EACH OTHER, TO THE LAND AND NATURE, TO OUR FOOD AND OUR COMMUNITIES.

Farmers, for instance, will need to form relationships with and be supported by customers who care about the social and ecological integrity of their food – not just its price or convenience. Consumers in this new food culture will be those who are seeking a more equitable relationship with nature and the earth, and this relationship, in part, will be facilitated through farmers.

But farms have other roles to play as well – for example, as centres of learning excellence and creative problem solving. Whether it's saving seeds, using biomass to generate power on the farm, regenerating rural communities or promoting biodiversity, organic farmers have a role to play in helping other farmers make the transition.

Our farms are also an important educational resource for both children and adults. Many have reskilling courses in food growing and crafts, and many run volunteer programmes. People taking part in these programmes are improving their own resilience for the future and gaining knowledge they can then pass on to others. By linking with CSAs (see Chapter 5) rural farms give urban dwellers a vital link to the land and to a sustainable future food supply.

NEW CENTRES OF

GROWING WELL

Low Sizergh Farm is a dairy farm located in the gentle, rolling hills of the southern Lake District in Cumbria. It also devotes six acres to growing organic vegetables, which are sold in the farm shop. The farm hosts educational visits for children and runs training programmes in horticulture open to everyone from the keen gardener to the professional. Diversifying in this way helps the farm create volunteer placements for local people. These placements are part of a Soil Association-certified social enterprise called Growing Well, which gives those recovering from mental health issues the opportunity to build their confidence and skills in a busy work environment. These volunteers undertake a diverse range of activities from seed sowing to financial management, tractor driving to web design.

EXCELLENCE

MUCH OF THE FIRST HALF OF THIS BOOK HAS ENCOURAGED SMALL-SCALE FARMING AND SELF-SUFFICIENCY AS A USEFUL HOBBY OR SIDELINE FOR ALL OF US. BUT TO ENSURE A SUSTAINABLE FUTURE WE WILL NEED MANY MORE PROFESSIONAL FARMERS WORKING THE LAND THAN WE HAVE NOW.

Government commitment in terms of education and investment priorities continues to encourage students to study maths and sciences. This is, of course, important, but the fact remains we need people who can feed us and know how to take care of the land.

With an average of 37 farmers leaving the land every day – many discouraged by the experience of conventional farming – our farming population is rapidly declining. The loss is much more than a body count, however; it is also a loss of skills and knowledge of how to produce good quality food, and care for the British countryside.

Our farming population is also ageing. The average age of a British farmer on a conventional farm is 56 and on an organic farm 49.

Although food security is a major concern, the government has yet to come up with a common sense approach to the necessity of producing more food within our national borders. The UK still imports 63% of its food and there has been little effort to change these statistics by, for example, putting more government resources into training or supporting a new generation of farmers interested in sustainable agriculture.

To face the future with confidence we need to recognise that organic methods are pivotal to regenerating the land and restoring agriculture to its central role in the UK economy. And we need to revitalise the workforce with younger farmers who can ensure it retains important skills as well as vitality and vision.

BE A FARMER

There is hope. All over the country, indeed all over the world, younger people are beginning to return to farming, fuelled by a determination to build a better world for themselves from the ground up.

The Soil Association's Organic Farm School, supported by the Daylesford Foundation, for example has more than 300 hands-on courses, including many on smallholding and animal rearing that provide a great way to learn more about farming techniques. **www.soilassociation. org/farmschool.aspx**

Small projects like Agrarian Renaissance in Hertfordshire, established in 2007, exist as exemplars for traditional, mixed, sustainable, high-welfare food and farming systems and can offer internships. **www. agrarianrenaissance.co.uk**

Reclaim the Fields is the European youth arm of Via Campesina, an international peasant farming movement that represents 800 million rural farmers from 60 countries who resist the globalisation of their lifestyles. The aim of Reclaim the Fields is to bring pressure to bear on politicians to re-localise the European economy in order to enable people to return to the land. They also aim to tackle climate change through farming reform, using the creativity and energy of young people to develop a sustainable European countryside. **www.reclaimthefields.org**

There are also apprenticeships. The Soil Association's Organic Apprenticeship Scheme is a two-year course involving a work-based placement with an organic farmer or grower. It provides hands-on experience and teaches the

practical skills needed for organic farming, as well as the principles and theory that underlie the organic philosophy. **www.soilassociation. org/apprentice.aspx**

The Biodynamic Agricultural Association also offers a practical two-year apprenticeship training in biodynamic agriculture. **www.biodynamic.org.uk**

CALL TO ACTION

ACT NOW

Make a connection with farmers in your area:

- Visit a farm shop and see if the farm is open to the public.

- Stop and talk to the farmer at the farmers' market and find out how he grows his produce.

- Contact your box scheme provider and ask if you can look around the growing space.

- Set up a buying group that sources meat direct from a farmer.

- Visit a Soil Association demonstration farm.

ACT TOGETHER

- Get WWOOF-ing and be part of a movement of people who volunteer on organic farms worldwide. WWOOF stands for World Wide Opportunities on Organic Farms. Member organisations link people who want to volunteer on organic farms or smallholdings with people looking for volunteer help. **www.wwoof.org**

ACT DIFFERENTLY

- Investigate a career in farming.

- When you vote, ask candidates about their stand on UK food security and sustainable farming.

- Think of our farmers as an extension of the health service – every delay in building a secure, healthy, sustainable food system adds to more illnesses and premature deaths, rising obesity and increased public costs of a poor national diet.

FIGHTING CLIMATE CHANGE IN THE SOIL

THINK CARBON SINKS AND YOU PROBABLY THINK OF TREES AND FORESTS. BUT SOIL IS THE BEST FORM OF CARBON STORAGE WE HAVE. IT CONTAINS THREE TIMES AS MUCH CARBON AS THE ATMOSPHERE AND FIVE TIMES AS MUCH AS FORESTS AND OTHER VEGETATION. BECAUSE OF THE SIZE OF THIS STORE, EFFORTS TO INCREASE SOIL CARBON LEVELS CAN HAVE VERY BENEFICIAL EFFECTS ON THE LEVEL OF ATMOSPHERIC CO_2. EVERY 1% INCREASE IN AVERAGE SOIL CARBON LEVELS COULD REDUCE ATMOSPHERIC CO_2 BY UP TO 2%.

Farmers have a key role to play in helping to increase carbon levels in our soil. Typically, soil contains about 45% minerals (soil particles), 25% water, 25% air and 2%–10% organic matter. Carbon is held in the soil's organic matter, which is made up of dead plant roots and leaves – the blackish-brown substance called humus – and living organisms such as earthworms, molluscs, nematodes, fungi, protozoa and bacteria. Of all these, humus is arguably the most stable and important carbon store. The level of humus changes slowly over time, so to increase the underlying level of carbon in the soil, farmers need to focus on increasing soil humus levels.

There are several different ways of doing this. There is a link between the use of inorganic nitrogen fertiliser and low soil carbon levels, so using fewer or no synthetic fertilisers is a good place to start. Instead, adding more organic matter in the form of animal manure, compost or ploughing in 'green manures' (cover crops that are planted between growing seasons) is essential to both improve soil quality and its carbon storing ability. Cover crops are particularly important, as their roots interact with living organisms such as fungi and earthworms in a way that encourages carbon storage: they create more stable 'aggregates' within the soil structure that have the effect of locking stable forms of carbon into the soil as organic matter decomposes.

Grasslands tend to store more carbon than arable land, so another way to increase carbon storage in the soil is for arable farms to build in 'fertility' breaks, during which some of their land is sown with grass and clover for a year or more. It would also help to raise grass-fed livestock, as this requires permanent grass pastures and reduces the amount of arable fields needed to produce grain for animal feed.

Any kind of farming system can use these practices, but all of them are essential in organic farming. It's no surprise, then, that studies in northern Europe show that organic farming stores 28% more soil carbon than non-organic systems. If we want our farmers to capture more carbon we need to encourage organic agriculture on a wider scale.

A SHORT WORD
with Peter Melchett

Policy Director of the Soil Association

FUTURE FARMING

FARMING IS AT A CRITICAL CROSSROADS. THE CURRENT INTENSIVE, INDUSTRIAL FOOD MODEL BASED ON HIGH INPUTS OF FOSSIL FUEL, GLOBAL SOURCING AND CENTRALISED DISTRIBUTION IS NEITHER SUSTAINABLE NOR RESILIENT AGAINST FUTURE SHOCKS.

Over the next 20 years we need to make fundamental changes to the way we farm, process, distribute, prepare and eat our food. We could continue with the 'business as usual' farming model – with its attendant pressures on resources, wildlife, landscapes, animal welfare and health. Or we could seek to re-balance our diets, and develop more resource-efficient, environmentally friendly methods of farming.

Sixty years ago the organic movement developed a system for producing food that proved there is another way. It's not a perfect system, but organic farming techniques already make a significant contribution towards the production of more climate-friendly food. Critics of organic farming claim it could never feed the world, suggesting food production would fall by half or more. Yet the current

system, turning oil into food, simply won't be available in the future. The real question we have to answer is how can we feed the world from systems of farming that do not rely on fossil fuels, and that do not contribute to climate change?

Organic farming aims to be an optimal output system, producing sufficient quantities of great quality food, without environmental or animal welfare compromises. It also helps us to store carbon. According to the Intergovernmental Panel on Climate Change, about 90% of agriculture's potential to cut GHGs lies in the storage of carbon in our soils – for example, by restoring the peatlands and adding carbon-rich organic matter to agricultural soils rather than relying on artificial fertiliser. Widespread adoption of organic farming practices in the UK would offset at least 23% of our agriculture's current GHGs – and about 1% of total global emissions. Research shows that organic techniques in northern Europe produce 28% higher soil carbon levels than non-organic farming.

It is possible to roll-out organic farming across the UK, but many things would have to change as this happened, particularly our eating habits. We would need to buy most of our food seasonally and locally. We would eat less, but better quality, eggs and dairy products, more grass-fed beef and lamb, more fruit and vegetables, and far less energy-intensive, grain-fed and industrially-reared chicken and pork, ending practices that raise significant animal welfare concerns. As a nation, we would enjoy a far healthier diet – one that can be delivered by organic farming as effectively as non-organic farming delivers our current, frequently unhealthy diet.

Research released in 2008 by the University of Reading created a model of what an organic UK would look like based on current patterns of production. The results are surprising. A wholly organic agriculture could actually produce more (and healthier) beef and lamb than we do now: production would rise to around 168% and 155% of current levels respectively. Chicken, egg and pork production would fall to roughly a quarter of current levels, with resulting massive reductions in energy use. The amount of wheat and barley we produce would drop by around 30%.

However, because we would be feeding far less grain to animals (currently half the cereals we grow are fed to animals), we could have as much wheat and barley for human consumption under an organic system as we have now.

On yield comparisons, production of field peas and beans would be similar to now, and production of oats and some other cereals might rise from current levels. If we stop growing sugar beet (already declining due to recent changes in European agricultural policy), we could grow a similar tonnage of potatoes as at present. Dairy production would fall by 30%–40%, unless herds were re-established and dairies re-opened in parts of the country that have lost them. Output of fruit and vegetables would be maintained and could increase should extra volumes be demanded, as organic yields are generally similar to non-organic.

If we want to continue eating huge quantities of cheap chicken, pork, dairy products, and other mass-produced processed food, organic farming can't deliver. But maintaining this diet, with its potentially severe consequences for human health, would saddle us with huge human, economic and environmental costs. The crisis of diet-related diseases and obesity is already costing the NHS £7.7 billion per year, and the cost to society as a whole is put at £20 billion. Our diets must, and inevitably will, change.

There would be many other benefits associated with a wholly organic agriculture. We would dramatically cut GHG emissions and water pollution. Energy-intensive inputs to farming would fall and jobs in rural areas would increase. Fertiliser inputs would drop by 95% and sprays by 98%, while farm employment would increase by 73%. Water use would fall, and farmland's capacity to act as a buffer to reduce flooding would strengthen. We would be building not eroding our precious soil, and there would be roughly 50% more wildlife in our countryside. For this to come about, we need a revolution in farming. As the University of Reading report concluded, 'organic agriculture is not simply conventional agriculture in miniature, it is different in management philosophy, scale and system'.

Ultimately, changing the way we farm means changing the way we eat. None of us is passive in the debate about how we will have to feed ourselves in the future. We can all make a difference: three times a day, every day.

"Changing the way we farm means changing the way we eat. None of us is passive in the debate about how we feed ourselves in the future."

07

GLOBAL FOOD

WE ARE ALL PARTICIPANTS IN THE GLOBAL FOOD MARKET.
WE REAP ITS BENEFITS AND WE ARE RESPONSIBLE FOR THE
DAMAGE IT DOES TO LAND AND LOCAL ECONOMIES. AS THE
WEATHER BECOMES MORE UNPREDICTABLE AND THE OIL
RUNS DRY, IT MAY BE WORTH ASKING OURSELVES:

IS IT TIME TO START THINKING SMALLER?

WHAT IS FOOD SECURITY?

EVERY ERA HAS A DEFINING ISSUE. SOMETHING THAT SHAPES, EVEN CHANGES, THE DIRECTION SOCIETY IS HEADING. IN THE 21ST CENTURY THAT ISSUE WILL BE GLOBAL FOOD SECURITY.

There is an understandable tendency when we think of climate change to point the finger of blame at oil companies, car manufacturers and the aviation industry. Certainly, there is a lot of long-standing data on the damage done by these industries. But in recent years the globalised food system has come under increased scrutiny and it has become clear that its role is just as damaging. The large amounts of fertilisers and pesticides used, the swathes of forest cut down to make way for farms, and the large amounts of energy consumed in transporting food, all make the system a major contributor to climate change. According to the Food and Agriculture Organisation (FAO), agriculture alone is responsible for around 30% of man-made GHGs.

Then there is the problem of an increasing population. Currently the world population stands at 6.6 billion: by 2050 the figure is expected to rise to 9.1 billion. This is going to put even greater pressure on our dwindling resources. The challenge, however, will not simply be producing enough food, but making sure that it reaches the people who need it, wherever they are in the world.

FACT:
According to the *Ecologist* magazine, around 69% of pesticides and 63% of primary energy used for agriculture in the UK are imported. In the EU, 70% of animal feed is imported and around 37% of fertilisers come from countries such as Russia, Norway, Egypt, Morocco, Tunisia, Libya, Ukraine and Belarus.

Tim Lang

For years, concerns about food security have focused only on developing countries where, for various reasons such as ongoing drought and poverty, there hasn't been 'enough'. The World Health Organisation defines food security as a state where 'all people at all times have access to sufficient, safe, nutritious food to maintain a healthy and active life'. In the face of a changing climate and dwindling natural resources, however, the issue of 'enough' could easily become a problem in the developed world too.

Availability and access to adequate nutrition is greatly complicated by the global nature of our food supply. Arguments for and against globalisation persist: can future food needs be met through current methods of production? Does food security need to be defined as national self-sufficiency? Is globalisation at the root of food insecurity, especially in rural communities, or does it cure it?

Politicians and captains of industry, wedded to the notion of a global market, sometimes dismiss the notion of national self-sufficiency as an illusion. They cite the extent to which goods produced in one country depend on inputs of gas, fertiliser, pesticides, feed and machinery produced elsewhere.

Because climate change and peak oil are global problems, the countries on which we depend for our imports are as vulnerable to their effects as we are. Government and industry refuse to re-envision what self-sufficiency might look like, which means that few, if any, common sense measures have been put in place to ensure that when we enter a period of energy descent, the UK can still feed itself without such a high reliance on inputs from other similarly stressed countries.

Groups like the Soil Association, which campaign for more low-input, local food production, are not 'anti-trade'. Nor are they seeking a return to the days of near 100% UK self-sufficiency (not seen in this country since the late 1800s).

What is needed is a national policy to relocalise production and distribution of our staple foods. Of course, we have to recognise that our tastes have changed and many people now expect bananas, coffee, avocados, rice, chocolate and so on as part of their regular diet. But indigenous foods such as vegetables, cereals, dairy and fresh meat should be produced as close to home as possible.

Given the vulnerabilities we face it is important that we find answers to some urgent questions, such as:

- How much food does the UK need to produce?

- Are there optimum levels of sustainable national self-sufficiency?

- How resilient is the UK's food supply?

- What kind of food should we eat to be healthy?

Find out more about the Soil Association's strategies for resilient food and farming at **www. soilassociation.org/ foodfutures.aspx**

PUSHING PRICES UP

Even if we weren't facing the prospect of climate change, pressure from a growing population alone could cause a huge rise in food prices. A recent report by the International Food Policy Research Institute (IFPRI), a Washington based organisation focusing on world hunger and agricultural policies, found that without climate change, wheat prices might rise from USD\$113 per tonne in 2000 to USD\$158 per tonne in 2050 – a 39% increase. Similarly, rice prices would soar by 62% and maize by 63%. Factor in climate change, however, and prices rise even more: wheat prices by at least 170%, rice by at least 113% and maize by at least 148% by mid-century.

WHEAT 39
RICE 62
MAIZE 63
PER CENT PRICE INCREASE
WITHOUT CLIMATE CHANGE

2050

WHEAT 170
RICE 113
MAIZE 148
PER CENT PRICE INCREASE
WITH CLIMATE CHANGE

IT CAN BE HARD TO THINK AHEAD. WALK IN TO ANY SUPERMARKET TODAY AND YOU MAY WONDER WHY YOU SHOULD. YOU MAY ASK WHETHER ALL THIS INDIVIDUAL EFFORT TO GROW YOUR OWN, SHOP LOCALLY AND INCREASE THE AMOUNT OF FRESH PRODUCE YOU EAT IS REALLY NECESSARY.

We are all participants in the global market. We reap its benefits and we are also responsible for the damage it does. Climate change is happening and if we want to feed the world in the future, we need to start making changes in how we eat and how we farm right now. If we don't, the prospects are grim.

The level of GHGs such as carbon dioxide, methane and nitrous oxide in the atmosphere was about 280ppm (parts per million) before the industrial revolution. It has been rising steadily ever since.

atmosphere by 80% by 2050. No industry is exempt from the need to cut emissions. This means that our farming and food system must change along with other sectors.

Extreme weather events are just one impact of global warming to worry about. But these could lead to an equally serious reduction in the amount of productive farmland. India, for instance, is on track to become the world's most populous country. But if the climate continues to change, there could be a 40% drop in India's agricultural

A CHANGING

WILL IT MAKE ANY REAL IMPACT? THE SHELVES ARE FULL; THE SYSTEM SEEMS TO BE COPING WITH THE FEW INTERRUPTIONS IN SUPPLY THAT WE EXPERIENCED IN 2007–08. SO WHY BOTHER?

These gases trap heat as they accumulate in the atmosphere, and as their levels rise our climate changes dramatically. Places that were once green farmland become deserts, while places where once there was ice begin to melt. And in many parts of the world there are more floods and other extreme weather events.

Scientists say we must not let levels of GHGs rise above 350ppm because of the damage it will do to our global climate. This is why many countries in the world have committed themselves to reducing the amount of CO2 in the

productivity by the 2080s due to predicted record heatwaves, which would bake its wheat-growing region. This would put hundreds of millions of people on the brink of chronic hunger.

India's neighbour Bangladesh faces a different challenge. Because it is such a low-lying country a rise in sea levels – caused by the melting of the glaciers in the Himalayas – could put most of the country underwater, displacing millions.

In Africa, where four out of five people make their living directly from the land, productivity could drop 30%, forcing farmers to abandon traditional crops in favour of more heat- and flood-resistant ones like rice. In some African countries, such as Senegal and war-torn Sudan, productivity is predicted to decline by 50% – which would amount to a total collapse of their agricultural systems.

Even Latin America, which has recently become a powerful productive force on the global market, could suffer crop reductions of 20% or more.

One of the most serious problems we face is the increasing unpredictability of the weather, with more drought in some areas and more floods in others. Sometimes this will happen in the same place, with the possibility of droughts followed by flash flooding. When the weather is too wet crops can become waterlogged or be difficult to harvest and store. When it is too dry they can fail to thrive.

Modern crops have been bred to grow well and resist pests and disease within the very narrow range of weather conditions they are usually exposed to. Wider variations in rainfall and drought inevitably lead to lower yields and greater risk of pests, forcing farmers to use more energy-intensive and polluting pesticides to prevent crop losses.

Drops in crop yields snake their way through the entire food system. It's not just your weekly loaf that will cost more. Because we feed much of our livestock on grain, meat prices will also rise, and supplies of everything will become scarce. Whatever the weather, it could mean less food for everyone.

These scenarios were starkly laid out in a 2009 report from the International Food Policy Research Institute (IFPRI), which estimates that in 2050 there will be 25 million more children malnourished than there are today due to the impact of climate change on global agriculture.

WHAT WILL HAPPEN IN THE UK?

If climate change continues unabated sea levels could rise between 26cm–86cm above the current level in south-east England by the 2080s. This could put 57% of Grade 1 farmland below sea level, and bring significantly increased risks of flooding, especially in East Anglia and most notably The Fens, which hold 37% of England's acreage for outdoor grown vegetables.

Higher temperatures will impact on crop yields. The average annual temperatures across the UK could rise by as much as 3.5°C by the 2080s, depending on future levels of GHGs. The unprecedented heatwave that affected Europe in 2000, when crop yields fell by 25%–30% across France and Italy, gave an unpleasant foretaste of what is predicted to become a more frequent event.

These forecasts may sound over the top, but they're not. Farmers are already noticing changes, such as earlier growing seasons, extreme weather events and increased droughts. A survey carried out in September 2008 by Farming Futures, a body set up by the government to advise farmers on how to handle climate change, found that 50% of farmers in England said they were already affected by climate change, and almost 70% expected to be affected in the next 10 years.

GREEN FINITE INFLATION
REVOLUTION
CLIMATE CHANGE
GLOBALISATION FOOD SOIL MARKET FORCES
SUPPLY EROSION
URBANISATION FARMER LEAVING THE LAND
INDIA PEAK OIL
BIOFUELS
CHINA WATER SHORTAGES
SALINIZATION
PEAK PHOSPHATE
POPULATION

PEAK EVERYTHING

MANY OF THE WORLD'S NATURAL RESOURCES ARE FINITE; THEY CAN'T BE REPLACED AND THEY ARE RUNNING OUT. WHEN DEMAND FOR A PARTICULAR RESOURCE IS HIGHER THAN THE RATE AT WHICH IT CAN BE REPLENISHED IT IS SAID TO REACH ITS 'PEAK'. AFTER THIS POINT SUPPLIES STEADILY DECLINE UNTIL EVENTUALLY THEY RUN OUT.

The notion of the 'peak' before the fall has been widely used to describe dwindling fossil fuel supplies, but in his 2008 book energy expert Richard Heinberg advanced the notion that our unabated use of global resources was leading to 'peak everything'. Because contemporary farming is so resource-intensive the decline of several key resources, as outlined by Heinberg, will inevitably impact on our future food supply.

PEAK OIL

Oil is a unique form of highly concentrated energy. Over the past 150 years it has been plentiful, cheap and the driving force behind phenomenal global economic and population growth. Supplies of natural gas have likewise helped to fuel a burgeoning economy. But our oil and gas supplies are running out and for businesses and economies that depend on the availability of cheap fossil fuels the consequences of this resource peaking are dire.

Reserves in the US, Canada, Norway and the UK are already in decline, while those in Saudi Arabia and Russia are rapidly approaching their peak. Oil is still being found (for instance, in Brazil, and possibly in the Arctic), but new reserves will be harder to access and therefore a lot more expensive and energy-intensive to produce. Extracting oil from sources such as tar sands and shale is not only environmentally devastating, it also requires huge amounts of energy that could lead, ultimately, to an energy deficit from these sources.

We have known since the mid-1950s that oil reserves would reach their peak in the early 21st century, and yet we have done nothing to reduce our consumption either individually or collectively.

Our food supply will be one of the first things affected by peak oil. Fossil fuels are needed for every stage of the process. Gas is used to make nitrate fertiliser. Oil is needed to produce pesticides, run tractors and transport food around the globe. Fossil fuels of all kinds are used to generate the electricity required for canning, freezing, pre-cooking and other food processes, as well as to refrigerate food in storage, in shops, supermarkets and our homes.

As oil runs out, the cost of all these activities will be passed on to the consumer. This is why we need to build greater resilience into our food supply by re-localising our food, growing more of our own, and changing our farming methods to rely less on synthetic inputs.

PEAK WATER

As with oil we imagine that water will always bubble up from the ground (or fall from the sky) in high enough quantities to meet our needs. But this may no longer be the case. Historically, people used to live beside rivers and lakes; water was a key means of communication as well as an essential resource for drinking supplies and farming. With the development of rail transport and roads people could live and travel anywhere – but they still needed water to survive. Irrigation has made living far away from water supplies possible, but it has taken its toll on global water sources. We are now taking it out of the ground and out of rivers at a faster rate than it can be replenished: in years to come, we may well be fighting wars over water.

Food has become one of our most water-intensive industries. Currently at least 70% of the freshwater taken from the ground is used in agriculture. Unless we can change these thirsty methods of crop production, we will struggle to provide enough food for everyone.

FACT:
It is estimated that the average Briton drinks between two and five litres of water per day and will use about 145 litres for cooking, cleaning, washing and flushing. However, if the embedded water used in the production of the goods we consume is also taken into account, the daily use per person in the UK may be nearer 3,400 litres. Food accounts for 65% of this.

FOOD	SERVING	WATER
TOMATO	70g	13l
POTATO	100g	25l
CUP OF TEA	250ml	35l
ORANGE	100g	50l
APPLE	100g	70l
CUP OF INSTANT COFFEE	125ml	80l
GLASS OF WINE	125ml	120l
SLICE OF BREAD	30g	135l
EGG	40g	135l
PINT OF BEER	568ml	170l
GLASS OF ORANGE JUICE	200ml	170l
BAG OF POTATO CRISPS	200g	185l
GLASS OF APPLE JUICE	200ml	190l
GLASS OF MILK	200ml	200l
HAMBURGER	150g	2,400l

Source: Waterwise, 2007

EMBEDDED WATER

As water supplies dry up the issue of embedded water (the 'hidden' water used to make products) is likely to become as important a measure of sustainability as food miles or CO_2 emissions. Consider the water used in growing and producing some common foodstuffs.

Notice how the amount of hidden water goes up when a food is processed (for example, from an apple to apple juice or from a potato to potato crisps). According to the 2007 report *Hidden Waters* by the group Waterwise, the average Briton consumes 3,400 litres of embedded water a day. We must also remember that when we buy foods from other countries we are also buying their water – and often these countries are already water-stressed. Each green bean stem from Kenya, for instance, contains four litres of embedded water.

PEAK SOIL

Good productive soil takes a long time to evolve. It requires a basic mixture of sand or silt, nutrients stored in plants, the continual interaction with soil microbes, worms and insects, and the addition of drying and rotting vegetation. It is estimated that it takes tens of thousands of years to create 15cm of topsoil, the rich crust on the earth's surface that makes farmland productive. In less than two centuries we've depleted this crucial resource – we are currently losing topsoil at a rate 10 to 20 times faster than it can naturally be replenished.

In intensive farming, nutrients are taken from the soil without replacing them. This degraded soil is then propped up with fertilisers derived either from oil or mined minerals. Synthetic fertilisers applied externally do not nourish the soil – any more than a synthetic moisturiser rubbed into your face can 'nourish' the skin.

But even if they could, we are now at a point of peak fertilisers as well. This is particularly true for supplies of nitrogen and phosphorus, arguably two of the most widely used 'Green Revolution' fertilisers. Nitrogen-based fertilisers are made from fossil fuels, principally natural gas, which is currently running out. Phosphorus comes from the world's phosphate mines, which, optimistically, have 90 years' worth of supplies left: a more pessimistic estimate puts this at 30. A sure sign of peak anything is sharp price rises and in the last two years the price of phosphorus has risen by 500%.

The most sustainable long-term solutions to peak soil involve designing farm systems, such as those used in organic farming, that build fertility through crop rotations, recycling nutrients and, increasingly, carbon capture (see Chapter 6).

Practising crop rotation – essential for both fertility and pest control in organic and other ecological farming methods – is the best way to maintain soil nitrogen levels. On intensive farms, fields are left bare for long periods of time after harvest. Simply planting a cover crop can significantly reduce nitrogen loss as well as limit soil erosion. Leguminous crops (such as clover, beans and pulses) introduced into the rotation cycle also help to fix nitrogen in the soil.

But this practice was abandoned on big farms because for 60 years it has been cheaper to apply fertilisers. This is no longer the case. A new approach is urgently needed to address climate change and resource depletion.

The phosphorus problem is in some ways more complex than that of fossil fuels; while it's possible to shift to alternative energy sources, phosphorus cannot be manufactured. It can, however, be recycled from animal and green manures, crop residues, food processing waste, communal organic and human waste.

But this process is made more risky by the fact that our sewage systems have also become a dumping ground for certain toxic wastes that we don't want anywhere near our food. To make sewage recycling safe we need scientists, engineers and governments to prioritise the development of separate waste streams for the disposal of pharmaceuticals, household chemicals and industrial wastes. This, in turn, requires a more holistic vision of the food system and how it fits into our everyday lives.

THE PROMISE OF BIOCHAR

One way of potentially improving soil fertility is through the addition of what is known as 'biochar'. Based on an ancient technique of burying charcoal in the ground, biochar is a charcoal-like material that can be produced from agricultural waste. Research in this method is in its early stages but early data suggests that adding biochar to soils can provide the structural habitat needed for a rich community of micro-organisms to take hold. It also suggests that biochar could reduce plants' need for nitrogen by 20%–30%, while also sequestering carbon that would otherwise end up in the atmosphere.

UNDER

IT'S NOT JUST CLIMATE CHANGE
AND RESOURCE DEPLETION
THAT THREATENS OUR FOOD
SUPPLY. YEARS OF INTENSIVE
FARMING HAVE LEFT THEIR MARK
TOO. TODAY THE DIETS OF THE
DEVELOPED WORLD RELY HEAVILY
ON JUST FOUR COMMERCIAL
CROPS — WHEAT, RICE, CORN AND
SOYA — VERY OFTEN CONSUMED
AS PROCESSED FOODS OR,
VIA ANIMAL FEED, AS MEAT.

Vast monocultures like these destroy not only local biodiversity but also genetic diversity. It is estimated that around three-quarters of the genetic diversity once found in agricultural crops has been lost over the past century.

Intensive farming practices also damage soil structure. Annual grain crops such as wheat require the land to be ploughed and cultivated anew each year. In between plantings the land is often left bare for lengthy periods of time. Without vegetative cover to lock carbon into the soil, CO_2 begins to escape into the atmosphere adding further to the burden of GHGs in our environment. Heavy inputs of fertilisers and pesticides (themselves CO_2-intensive to produce) speed this process up and upset the natural mineral balance of the soil, making it more vulnerable to erosion by wind and rain.

Around the world soils are eroding at an alarming rate. In Europe, the current rate of soil loss from farmlands is 15 times greater than the estimated average rate of natural soil erosion in prehistoric times. Globally, it is estimated that every year the amount of soil washed downstream in rivers is the equivalent of four tonnes per person on the planet.

Increasingly, salty soils are another problem. This occurs as rising water tables bring saline compounds to the surface as a result of deforestation, clearing land of deep-rooted, perennial crops, or over-irrigation. Saline soils can have a devastating impact on crop yields. Of the world's 230 million hectares of irrigated agricultural land, some 45 million hectares are currently salt-affected, and of the 1,500 million hectares of non-irrigated arable land, 32 million hectares face problems with salt contamination.

PRESSURE

FOOD OR FUEL?

Another big pressure on land comes from diverting food crops into biofuels. Food is just one of many commodities in the global market, which means it doesn't matter whether the end user is a person or an animal or a car. What matters is the market price.

As our oil runs out more and more crops are being diverted into biofuels, putting our food supply and the needs of one billion starving people in direct competition with planes, trains and automobiles. Turning plants into fuels requires additional energy and water. In countries like India and China where fuel crops are irrigated the process can use an extra 3,500 litres of water for every litre of biofuel. Even in the US where many crops are rain-fed it takes an additional 400 litres of groundwater to produce a litre of ethanol.

Some people see the big oil companies' investment in plant-derived fuels as a positive move allowing us to maintain our energy-hungry lifestyles. But in the end it could seriously undermine the food needs of the poor and the environmental needs of the planet.

At the same time, our participation in the global market, where food is shipped thousands of miles around the world, is eating up fuel. The number of food miles accumulated by many of the everyday products we take for granted is staggering and the CO_2 emissions from this is a direct contributor to the catastrophic problem of global warming. For example, the Soil Association calculates that:

9.63 TONNES

of CO_2 emissions is produced by the average person through the food he or she eats.

1.1 TONNES

is added to per capita emissions by a weekly basket of imported food for a family of four.

49,000 MILES

is the distance a typical Sunday meal could travel – equivalent to two journeys around the world, releasing 37kg of CO_2.

50 TIMES MORE CO_2

is emitted by distributing products by plane than by sea freight.

FOR EVERY 1,000 FRUIT PRODUCTS

bought in the UK only six will have been grown here.

40 PER CENT OF ALL UK ROAD FREIGHT

is taken up by the food system.

Changing your eating behaviour to source more of your diet locally is a great first step to reducing your carbon footprint. But no single action will help us reach the 80% cut in GHG emissions that we need in order to prevent runaway global warming. Biofuels are a dangerous distraction from the real issue: we need to cut down on all our transport – of people and of food – if we are going to make a real difference and make it in time.

FOOD JUSTICE

FEW COUNTRIES CAN HOPE TO BE 100% SELF-SUFFICIENT, ESPECIALLY NOW THAT TASTES HAVE CHANGED AND DEMAND FOR FOODS LIKE CHOCOLATE AND COFFEE HAVE GIVEN GREATER VARIETY TO OUR LIVES. BUT THE PROBLEMS OF GLOBALISATION BECOME MORE OBVIOUS IN A WORLD DOMINATED BY CLIMATE CHANGE AND PEAK OIL. THE GLOBALISED FOOD SYSTEM ASSUMES THAT OUR RESOURCES – FUEL, LAND, WATER, CLIMATE AND HEALTHY SOIL – ARE PREDICTABLE AND INFINITE. YET NONE OF THESE THINGS CAN BE COUNTED ON IN THE FUTURE.

Greater resilience in the food supply is often given as a reason for taking part in the global marketplace. The logic is that, if a company can't source a commodity from one country – because, for example, the harvest is lower that year, or there is political unrest – then it can be sourced from somewhere else, thus keeping the 'flow' of food around the world moving.

But the more this system is challenged by climate change and peak oil the more we see that such resilience is little more than robbing Peter to pay Paul. In fact, the same behaviour that has led to the recent global financial collapse – mortgaging the future to pay for today – is now leading to a collapse of the food system.

WORKERS' RIGHTS

Where does your food come from? Who grows it?

At present, half the world's workforce – 1.1 billion workers – is employed in agriculture. Of this number, only 450 million (40%) are in waged labour, 170 million are children and nearly 300 million are women working for lower wages than their male counterparts, often in the export trade.

Throughout the world farm workers are denied basic rights that many of us take for granted, such as:

- overtime pay
- a minimum wage
- restrictions on child labour
- attention to basic health and safety issues
- the right to join labour unions and bargain collectively.

If our food system is going to be clean and fair in the future these issues must be addressed. One advantage of re-localising our food system is that it makes the issue of farm labour rights more transparent by bringing it right to our doorsteps. Instead of the issue affecting some anonymous person in a faraway country, it may well be affecting a neighbour or a family member. Making the issues more visible and local may eventually force us to demand better treatment for farm labourers everywhere.

FOOD POLICY

The food we eat often has a hidden provenance. Not only are the people who produce it invisible to us, the politics that puts it on our tables are often shrouded in mystery.

Following the Second World War, when parts of Europe came close to starvation, there was a massive push at government level to produce more food, both in Europe and the US. One of the key tools in this policy was the introduction of production subsidies such as the Common Agricultural Policy in Europe. These subsidies have paid farmers in the developed countries to grow large commodity monocrops such as wheat, maize and soya, even when there was no immediate domestic demand. The overall effect has been to lower artificially the cost of production, which has in turn lowered the market price.

The combination of low prices and oversupply leads to the 'dumping' of surpluses in the global marketplace at prices that unsubsidised farmers in the developing world cannot compete with. This has created a market in which it is cheaper for developing nations to import (subsidised) staple foods from rich nations, and encourage their own farmers to concentrate on growing cash crops for export – in order to raise cash to buy imported staples.

The net effect of all this complicated global horse-trading is that, while there is more than enough food in the world to feed us all, around a billion people in developing nations are going hungry each day. Current international food and farming policies destroy domestic production of staple crops, damage soil fertility and leave many countries vulnerable to extreme weather events or other forms of instability that impact on food supplies.

Food and farming policy should not be about putting up barriers to international trade, but about encouraging re-localised food policy as an international norm. Likewise, if there have to be subsidies, these should be applied to encourage environmental responsibility, rather than to increase yields that are then dumped on world markets.

A global system of strategic food planning, which puts environmental and dietary needs at its centre, would encourage sustainable food systems, while creating space for trade in commodities that cannot be produced domestically.

HOMEMADE FAIR TRADE?

Many people are working very hard, often in difficult, hazardous and poorly paid conditions, to provide food for the world. This is the reality the Fairtrade movement has set out to counter, arguing that urban consumers barely know where their food comes from and need to re-engage with the reality of working on the land.

But while fair trade brings us ethical exotic goods from far away, it's worth asking why are there no domestic fairtrade labels for fruit and veggies, milk, cheese and beef? This is the issue being addressed by farmers in Mexico, who in 2001 set up the first domestic fairtrade label, Comercio Justo. In other, more developed countries, there has been little progress towards creating domestic fairtrade marks.

Even if we are not closer to creating a domestic fairtrade label in the UK, we can still help invest in fairer trade here by buying organic foods that are locally and ethically produced. The transparency of goods sold locally provides a kind of grass-roots quality control. You can speak directly with farmers about their products and practices, and if these aren't what they should be, word will soon spread.

> **FACT:**
> A Swedish farmhand needs to work for just five minutes to earn enough to buy one kilo of cereals at the local market.
> A farmhand in India will need to work 37 minutes.
> A farmhand in the Central African Republic will need to work for six hours.

READ ANY NEWSPAPER AND YOU COULD BE FORGIVEN FOR THINKING THAT THE SOLUTION TO OUR GROWING FOOD CRISIS LIES IN THE LAB, NOT ON THE FARM. INCREASINGLY, GENETIC MODIFICATION (GM) IS BEING HERALDED AS THE ANSWER TO OUR PROBLEMS. THROUGH GM, WE ARE TOLD, WE CAN PRODUCE SALT-TOLERANT PLANTS, DROUGHT-TOLERANT PLANTS AND CROPS THAT PRODUCE HIGHER YIELDS. THERE'S ONLY ONE CATCH. THESE GM MIRACLES DON'T EXIST.

Scientists who make salt- and drought-tolerant varieties 'work' under laboratory conditions consistently find that they fail to grow outdoors. Some believe it will be never be possible to produce such crops because the combinations of genes involved are too complex. No patent exists for a high-yield GM plant. Any gains in yield have been due to the initial resistance to pests or herbicides conferred by genetic manipulation. These gains are often short lived, however, because both pests and plants quickly develop resistance in a way that makes the GM traits less effective.

NO MIRACLE SOLUTIONS

Only two GM traits have ever made it to market – herbicide resistance (enabling a crop to withstand herbicide sprays) and Bt toxin expression (containing a strain of the naturally occurring Bacillus thuringiensis bacterium to kill any pests that might eat the plant). Other promises of genetic modification have failed to materialise, such as GM 'golden rice' to cure vitamin A deficiency, or GM carrots to cure osteoporosis.

CONTAMINATION

GM can't be contained. Once we start growing GM varieties, they will remain in the environment forever. Pollen from GM crops can cross-fertilise with non-GM crops. If we go down the route of this technology, the day will soon come when we can't be sure if the food we are eating is GM contaminated or not. In recent years, US farmers have successfully gone to court to stop the introduction of GM alfalfa and GM sugar beet. In both cases the court ruled that it was illegal to introduce crops which would cause wide spread contamination as it would deny the right of farmers to grow non-GM varieties.

MORE PESTICIDES

GM crops frequently increase farmers' reliance on pesticides. Herbicide resistant crops were developed to allow farmers to spray weeds without causing crop damage. But, increasingly, weeds are developing a resistance to the herbicides and as a result have to be sprayed first with a primary herbicide and then with various other herbicides to kill those that might have developed a resistance to the first treatment.

NOT PROVEN SAFE

GM has never been properly tested on humans and so never been proved safe for consumption. Tests on animals have revealed alarming health effects including damage to internal organs, sterility, growth defects and premature death of offspring. The only trial ever to involve human beings, in 2002, showed that altered genetic material from GM soybeans not only survives in the human gut, but may even be passed to bacteria within the digestive system.

NOT CHEAPER TO BUY

GM crops are subject to the same price hikes as other crops – the annual inflation rate for GM soya meal from Argentina for the year to May 2008 was 112.5%.

HIGHER COSTS TO FARMERS

GM crops cost farmers and governments more money than they make. The Soil Association estimates that the cost to the US economy of GM crops has been around USD$12 billion (£6 billion) since 1999, due to inflated subsidies for GM farms, loss of export orders and various seed recalls. In India, according to government figures, nearly 183,000 farmers committed suicide between 1997 and 2007. While biotech companies dismiss the notion, campaigners such as Prince Charles and the Indian farming group Navdanya believe that these suicides are related in part to the high cost of GM seeds and the subsequent failure of these crops to produce the promised high yields.

LOWER YIELDS

In spite of its many promises GM technology has not increased the yield of commercial crops. GM soybeans, for example, produce on average 6% lower yields than conventional varieties. Canadian trials show that Bt maize yields were, at best, the same as conventional varieties and that some Bt maize hybrids had a 12% lower yield then non-GM maize.

WHAT ABOUT GM?

PRIVATE CONTROL OF SEEDS

The introduction of new seed traits serves the interests of society as a whole, which is why research has traditionally been done by public institutions such as universities. The introduction of patented GM seeds has shifted this control to a handful of private companies. This monopoly is already having an impact: between 1975 and 2000 soybean seed prices rose by 63% in the US; this decade, in which GM seeds have come to dominate the US market, prices have risen 230%, affecting farm income and ultimately consumer prices.

STILL EATING OIL

GM crops do not reduce the need for chemical fertilisers in order to achieve expected yields. This means that GM crops are just as dependent on fossil fuels for fertilisers as conventional crops.

GLOBALISED FOOD SYSTEMS LEAVE PEOPLE HUNGRY

IN THE GLOBALISED FOOD SYSTEM BIGGER IS OFTEN CONSIDERED BETTER. FACED WITH A FOOD CRISIS OUR INTUITIVE RESPONSE IS TO MAKE LARGER, MORE INTENSIVE FARMS TO GROW MORE FOOD, USING MORE FERTILISERS, PESTICIDES AND NEW TECHNOLOGIES. THE SUGGESTION THAT WE NEED GM AND PESTICIDES TO FEED THE WORLD IS MADE INCREASINGLY OFTEN BY THE PR DEPARTMENTS OF BIG AGRIBUSINESS.

But this claim isn't backed up by evidence. Even if you ignore the future resource constraints that such farming methods will face, there is a persistent myth about the efficiency and productivity of big industrial farms that simply doesn't stand up to scrutiny.

Again and again studies show that small farms can be more productive than big ones. With a large monoculture simple yield calculations are made regarding the amount of one specific food commodity from a given unit of land. On a smaller farm, where polyculture (growing many different crops) is the norm, productivity is measured differently.

Smaller scale farmers using crop rotation will grow several different crops over subsequent seasons. The yield is therefore measured not by a single crop over one year, but by several crops over a number of years. With intercropping and companion planting several crops are grown on the same field at the same time. For example, fruit trees act as shade trees for coffee plantations, and fodder grass (*Desmodium*) grown around a primary crop (such as maize) deters pests.

Results from studies in the developing world are encouraging. In Brazil, growing onions and arracacha (a root vegetable) in separate fields required nearly 50% more land to produce the same yield as when they were grown together. In Ethiopia, wheat and faba beans grown together produced about 20% more than when grown on two separate fields; the intercropped field also had 20% fewer weeds and 30% less viral damage to the beans.

The increased yields of small farms can also be attributed to the more efficient use of land, water, biodiversity and other agricultural resources. The broader 'portfolio' of crops also makes much more sense in an unpredictable climate. Farmers growing single crops are much more dependent on the certainty of consistent weather conditions.

In the developing world – which is currently short of food and about to bear the brunt of climate change and population growth – the data shows that this small-farm, polyculture model, in tandem with the most up-to-date organic techniques, can increase whole farm yields significantly. In 2006, research carried out by Catherine Badgley at the University of Michigan showed that yields on small-scale organic farms in tropical regions were 50% higher than non-organic farms; a study by the UN Conference of Trade and Development in the same year found yields on organic farms in Africa to be 116% higher than on non-organic ones. While these farms will produce plenty of food, it will not, of course, be the kind of high-fat, high-protein, processed food that Western diets have become accustomed to.

For both the food and farming industries 'business as usual' is no longer an option – expensive oil, expensive inputs and climate change will see to that. And equally for food consumers a 'food as usual' mentality is not an option either. We all need to develop a sustainable diet based on pulses, seasonal fruit and vegetables, starchy carbohydrates, wholegrains and better quality grass-fed meat.

To achieve this, we urgently need a reform of the trade environment, and we urgently need greater investment in organic and other agro-ecological and sustainable farming techniques. If we can make these changes to both our diets and our way of life, then the world would be able to feed itself organically without recourse to harmful industrial techniques. If we can't, then we are in serious trouble. We are all stakeholders in the future of our food supply and we all have a responsibility to ensure that these necessary changes happen.

CALL TO ACTION

Through our food choices we all participate in the global food market. Therefore we all have a role to play in making it fairer, more environmentally friendly and more accessible to everyone.

ACT NOW

- Eat organic. By choosing organic produce you are encouraging planet-friendly farming.

- Buy fairtrade goods when you can.

- Reduce your food miles. Prioritise local and seasonal foods.

- Support your local seed bank – most require donations to survive. Why not adopt a seed and help save a species today?

ACT TOGETHER

- Say no to GM. Tell your supermarket and your politicians that you want the food supply to be GM-free.

- Form a local buying group and source your produce from nearby.

- Support food co-ops that provide ethical goods from abroad that can't be produced locally – such as spices, coffee and chocolate.

ACT DIFFERENTLY

- Buy fair trade whenever you buy goods from faraway countries.

- Fight food waste. If you shop weekly buy only what you need and what you know you can eat in the week (see Chapter 1).

SUPPORT SEED BANKS

MAINTAINING A DIVERSITY OF LOCAL CROPS IS IMPORTANT FOR THE HEALTH AND SUSTAINABILITY OF GLOBAL AGRICULTURE

The big four crops that feed most of the developed world have had much of their resilience to changes in climate and pests bred out of them. The resilience they do still have is largely due to external inputs like pesticides and fertilisers. In contrast, local crop varieties have an inbred resilience that makes them less vulnerable to changes in climate and soil. Through traditional plant breeding we can develop new, more globally resilient, more high yielding plant varieties to help preserve food supplies in the future.

One very important way to preserve resilience and biodiversity for the future is through the work of the world's seed banks.

More than 30,000 of the world's plant species are edible but only 7,000 have been domesticated: the other 23,000 are wild foods vital in maintaining the gene pool and providing a buffer against starvation. Of those 7,000 domesticated species, only 30 are cultivated commercially: wheat, corn and rice alone account for more than half of the food we consume globally.

Seed banks are a large-scale version of the seed saving many of us do at home. They act as an insurance policy against future disasters, categorising and storing seeds for all the world's plants in secure, climate controlled facilities.

They are vital because if climate change, disease, or natural or man-made disasters were to threaten a particular plant species, the unique characteristics of certain other varieties may be needed to build a resilient food supply in the future. For example, in the 1970s a widespread fungus cut US corn yields in half. The blight was alleviated by use of genetic materials from a wild corn relative that was fungus-resistant.

There are currently about 1,400 seed banks around the world, and each one stores a different range of seeds. Some of them focus on protecting local varieties, wildflowers or speciality vegetables. In the UK, the Millennium Seed Bank at Kew concentrates on wild plants and has so far stored seeds from 10% of the world's species. Others, like the Svalbard Global Seed Vault in Norway, also known as the Doomsday Vault, take a more global view. This vault is a backup for all other seed banks in the world.

For more information on seed banks visit **www.kew.org/science-conservation/conservation-climate-change/millennium-seed-bank/index.htm**

FOOD SECURITY

INTERNATIONAL TRADE IN AGRICULTURAL PRODUCE IS NOT NEW. TAKE SPICES AND COTTON FROM INDIA: THESE NEED VERY SPECIAL CLIMATES AND SOILS TO GROW AND HAVE BEEN EXPORTED FOR CENTURIES. WHAT IS NEW IS THE INCREASINGLY HEAVY TOLL THAT TODAY'S GLOBALISED FOOD SYSTEMS ARE TAKING ON THE PLANET AND ITS PEOPLE.

While globalisation of the food supply is often celebrated as a triumph, it is in many respects a tragedy. Those in the affluent North who believe that importing lettuce and green beans from Africa, and broccoli and barley corn from India, helps the poor in the South are ignoring a number of basic issues.

There is an intimate connection between globalisation, the number of farmers who are pushed out of farming, how many species disappear, how much GHG emissions increase, and how many children die of hunger.

Firstly, the poor are displaced to make way for the corporate farms that export fruit and vegetables. Transfer of land from peasants to corporations is the first negative impact of an agriculture based on the export of temperate produce from tropical countries. In India's Punjab huge land conflicts have been triggered by the appropriation of land belonging to small farmers for corporate farms growing vegetables for large supermarket chains. Those that remain in farming become workers on corporate farms, instead of being sovereign producers on their own land.

Secondly, an export agriculture controlled by corporations uproots local peasants, creates hunger and poverty and destroys local agro-biodiversity. It also blocks the potential for localisation in importing countries. The long-distance transport of food pollutes the atmosphere with carbon dioxide emissions from fossil fuels, and since vegetables and fruits are perishable their long-distance trade is highly energy-intensive.

175

The greatest tragedy of all is that while commodity markets grow, people starve. More than a billion people are now permanently hungry. Most of them are from rural areas. Many of them are food producers who are denied food either because their soils have been desertified, or because chemical agriculture and costly seeds have got them into debt, or because they are growing cash crops like cotton and coffee, which no longer provide an income because globalised trade has pushed down farm prices.

In our organic farm at Navdanya, we are actively involved in the rejuvenation of indigenous knowledge and farming culture and have helped create awareness of these issues. Our work on the farm is guided by four core principles around organic and local.

First, we must provide food for the soil and her millions of micro-organisms. The Green Revolution, with its chemical-intensive dwarf varieties, kills the soil organisms and breeds varieties with less straw. As a result no organic matter is returned to the soil. Genetic engineering of herbicide-resistant crops like Roundup Ready soya and corn also kills vegetation that would have gone back to feed the soil. Feeding markets while starving the soil is a recipe for hunger and desertification.

Second, it is important to feed the farming family. Small farmers are protectors and custodians of our vital and collective natural heritage

– our soils, our biodiversity, our water and even our air. It is criminal that they should themselves be going hungry. That is why we ensure that every producer family that is a member of Navdanya grows healthy and nutritious foods for the household first and only trades in surplus produce.

The third principle is to provide food for local communities. If local communities do not eat what is grown locally, their food will come from somewhere far away. And it will be more contaminated and adulterated and less safe. If local communities do not eat local produce, biodiversity will disappear from our farms, and cultural diversity will disappear from our diets, making both the land and its people poorer.

Finally, long-distance trade and exports are restricted to unique products. Different vegetables and fruits grow in different climates. Every culture on earth has evolved its own unique diet according to its particular ecosystem. Food staples must, as far as possible, be grown locally, both to produce what the ecosystem is best suited for, and to produce what local cultures have adapted themselves to.

It is wrong to grow temperate zone vegetables in the tropics and fly them back to rich consumers. Trade in food must be restricted to what cannot be grown locally, what is of high value, yet has a small ecological footprint in terms of use of land and water. Spices, for

instance, are a perfect candidate for long-distance trade. Spices grow in very specific ecosystems and only tiny quantities are needed to add flavour to food. They give high value with low volumes. This benefits the producer who can also grow crops for food. In Karnataka, spice growers use 10% of their land for spice gardens of pepper, cardamom and areca nut, and 10% for paddy for local consumption. These gardens have existed for centuries and are a model for farming that supports trade but is not destroyed by it.

Localisation of food systems is a climate change imperative. But it is also a food sovereignty and human rights imperative because small farmers will only survive in the context of vibrant and robust local food economies. Localisation is also a food security imperative. Short supply chains ensure better quality food, more freshness and more cultural diversity. They also ensure that everyone gets to eat.

Small farmers will only survive in the context of vibrant and robust local food economies. Localisation is a food security imperative.

THE WORLD IS CHANGING RIGHT BEFORE OUR EYES

WE CAN SEE THE EVIDENCE AND EFFECTS OF GLOBAL WARMING RIGHT NOW IN THE FREQUENCY OF UNPREDICTABLE WEATHER EVENTS, THE MELTING OF THE POLAR ICE CAPS AND THE PRICE OF OUR DAILY BREAD. THE SHEER SPEED WITH WHICH ALL THIS IS HAPPENING IS FRIGHTENING. THE REALITY OF CLIMATE CHANGE IS NO LONGER SOMETHING FAR OFF IN THE DISTANCE. IT IS RUSHING TOWARDS US LIKE A FREIGHT TRAIN.

We don't have to be helpless in the face of these changes. You may not think of yourself as an activist. You probably don't tie yourself to a tree regularly, or rush headlong into the path of a huge whaling ship in a small rubber dinghy, or stand on a busy runway as part of a human chain. This is the kind of activism that grabs headlines and sometimes changes the world.

But there are other types of activism that can also have an impact: daily, consistent, informed, intelligent efforts to bring about change by large groups of people. This is where we can all get involved.

It's too easy to feel that we are victims of some process beyond our control. But in reality, we are in the driver's seat. We are all participants in a consumer society and we can use our buying power either to fund social injustice and environmental collapse, or as a weapon to overcome these challenges.

The evidence of recent years is that we are more and more willing to use our consumer rights to become advocates for a better world. This is particularly true when it comes to food. Our food buying habits are already changing: we buy more organic food and more fairly traded food; the number of people using box schemes and farmers' markets has grown. At present the number of 'ethical shoppers' – people who buy goods that reflect their own ethical values – is on the rise, but it needs to grow more – and faster.

In 2008 every household in the UK spent, on average, £707 in line with their ethical values, up from £630 two years earlier. In particular, spending on ethical and organic food and drink was up 14% from £5.1 billion to £5.8 billion. This is encouraging, but still, with a total annual consumer spend of more than £600 billion, our overall ethical spending a year, at around £35.5 billion, remains very small.

We also need to recognise that there are things we buy and there are things we buy into, less consciously – for example, the idea of unrestricted economic growth and the need for a globalised food market. We should not take for granted the habits and mindsets of consumerism, such as slavish brand loyalty and the belief that the price you pay at the till is all that matters. These assumptions dictate our lifestyles and run the world. Instead, we should define ourselves as more than just consumers.

Right now developed countries – which account for just 20% of the world population – are consuming more than 80% of the world's natural resources. This causes a disproportionate level of environmental damage and a grossly unfair distribution of food and wealth. If we want to change this, then substituting the unsustainable food products in our shopping baskets with ones that are fairly traded and organically grown is only a first step.

There is a scientific and governmental reticence about tackling the issue of sustainable farming and food consumption. There is still a widespread belief that market forces alone should determine how we farm and how we eat. In particular, eating is seen as an individual lifestyle choice that cannot and should not be controlled or dictated from above.

This is only partly true. A choice is only individual when it does not affect others. Maintaining or even increasing our reliance on a food system that uses vast amounts of natural resources and pollutes the planet so prodigiously will clearly have a harmful impact on others. This is why it will require both consumer and governmental action to aid our evolution into a sustainable society.

THE NEW FOOD CULTURE

This book has been written to encourage us all to think about food choices and food issues, from the kitchen to the farm to the global marketplace; to show how food is interlaced with every area of our lives; to highlight how our food choices say something about our values as a society; and to draw sensible connections between the personal and the political, and provide a roadmap for activism at each level.

Through our belief in consumerism and market growth it has become our inclination to look to the future and think bigger. But it may be that thinking smaller proves more productive – revolutionary even. Rather than seeing the globe as a giant supermarket at our disposal, and looking for expensive, resource-intensive techno-fixes when shortages arise, the new food culture proposed in this book will make our lives simpler, more connected and healthier.

For this new food culture to take hold, however, we need a revolution in our sense of responsibility – to ourselves, to others and to the planet. In recent decades food has become someone else's responsibility. Now we are beginning to take that responsibility back. Doing so comes with a mixture of feelings: on the one hand, there is reluctance and resistance as we face a steep learning curve; but on the other, there is a sense of empowerment, excitement and adventure, and maybe even hope that our planet can once again become a great place to live.

We are standing at a time when the world faces many serious challenges, including climate change, population growth, fossil fuel depletion, water shortages, loss of biodiversity and possible food shortages. But in this moment we are also being given the opportunity to choose solutions that work.

In our own daily lives we can be less wasteful in the kitchen, read labels, shop with greater awareness of seasons and the environment, and learn new ways of cooking and storing food.

In our gardens, we can start growing vegetables and herbs on patios and windowsills, making even the smallest spaces into organic, productive, wildlife-friendly sources of food for our families.

Changes in the food culture of our communities and schools can reflect the more sustainable food system we'd like to see take hold throughout society. Thinking globally and acting locally is the best place to start: we can set up buying groups and community supported agriculture projects, work allotments and participate in landshare schemes, educate children from an early age about the importance of good food – and make sure they eat it every day at school.

We also have an opportunity to re-envision our cities as productive and sustainable places, rather than as food deserts. We can meet at least some of the food needs of urban areas through city farms, guerrilla allotments and rooftop gardens.

On the farm, both in the UK and globally, we can expand the reach of organic agriculture, begin to rebuild our soil, make better use of available resources, increase yields where possible and invite more young people to bring their energy and enthusiasm into farming. We can also lobby governments to stop subsidising our wasteful lifestyles and environmental degradation, and to direct more money into the land and sustainable agriculture than into genetic modification in the lab.

BUT THE MOST IMPORTANT THING ANY OF US CAN DO IS SIMPLY GET INVOLVED

Read, become informed, support forward-looking organisations such as the Soil Association, Friends of the Earth and Common Ground, start gardening groups, turn your town into a Transition Town, have debates, share your knowledge and experience. Above all, spread the word that our food system has to change, and that these changes will mean a cleaner agricultural system and a fairer share for everyone.

FEAST OR FAMINE?
FAMINE?
STUFFED OR STARVED?

WHICH WILL IT BE?
AND WHAT PART WILL YOU
PLAY IN MAKING IT HAPPEN?

A SHORT WORD

with Eric Schlosser

Author of *Fast Food Nation* (2001)
and contributing author to *Food, INC* (2009)

ORGANIC STRENGTH

IF YOU BELIEVE EVERYTHING YOU READ IN THE BRITISH NEWSPAPERS, ORGANIC FOOD IS NO HEALTHIER THAN FOOD PRODUCED WITH HERBICIDES AND PESTICIDES. IN FACT, ORGANIC FOOD IS 'ELITIST' – A COSTLY EXTRAVAGANCE FOR RICH PEOPLE AND CELEBRITIES – WHILE GM CROPS ARE ESSENTIAL TO PREVENT MASS STARVATION IN POOR COUNTRIES.

People who buy organic food are therefore gullible, trendy, foolish and ultimately heartless. If all that is true, then it's the multinational chemical companies who care the most about the poor. It's the agribusiness companies who care the most about protecting the environment. And it's the fast food chains who care the most about your health. Perhaps we should disband the Soil Association immediately, buy some GM seeds to plant them in our gardens and go around the corner for a Big Mac.

The backlash against the organic movement is in full swing, quietly funded and eagerly promoted by the corporations threatened by its success. George Orwell would be impressed by the misinformation that's being spread. He would have enjoyed the notion that the corporations responsible for today's crises in agriculture, the environment and public health now claim to know the only possible solutions. And he would have been the first to tell you never to believe everything you read in the paper.

Farmers, activists and consumers who have championed organics for years don't like to see themselves vilified. Things are tough at the moment, and the current economic downturn has increased the appeal of cheap foods, regardless of their origin. But today's well-funded and well-organised attacks against the organic movement are a clear sign of its underlying strength. For decades after the founding of the Soil Association, the campaign on behalf of sustainable agriculture was largely ignored. Then it was ridiculed, with much comment in the press about Prince Charles talking to his plants. And now we are supposed to believe that there really is no difference between an organic strawberry and one doused with chemical poisons, that GM crops are the way forward and that the Soil Association's policies may cause the deaths of millions. A quote of Mahatma Gandhi's comes to mind: 'First they ignore you, then they laugh at you, then they fight you, then you win.'

The proponents of industrial agriculture and industrial food spend billions of pounds every year promoting their agenda. The marketing budget of the organic movement is insignificant by comparison. But the movement has an invaluable asset on its side: the truth. The way that we produce food has changed more in the past 40 years than in the previous 40,000. And the evidence is conclusive that this industrialised system cannot be sustained. Within 40 years it has caused widespread environmental devastation, contaminated rivers and streams and groundwater, spread new forms of infectious diseases, launched epidemics of obesity and diabetes, driven small farmers off the land and imposed terrible cruelties on livestock and low-wage workers. This system is not sustainable, it's incredibly fragile. And without cheap fossil fuels, it will collapse.

Instead of an arrogant and futile effort to control nature, we need a set of agricultural practices that seek to work with nature. We need a renewed sense of humility. This does not mean eliminating the use of all technology. It means regarding every new technology with a healthy scepticism – and ensuring a careful scrutiny of the potential consequences. We were once assured that feeding dead cattle to cattle was a good idea, an efficient use of resources. Anyone who disagreed was attacked, belittled, dismissed as alarmist. The lesson to be learned from that fiasco isn't that we all should become Luddites. It's that an industry's short-term desire for profits should never take precedence over a society's long-term survival.

With billions to spend on clever ads, fancy websites and celebrity endorsements, the industrial food system may seem invincible. But nothing could be further from the truth. This system is extremely vulnerable. Once people see where this industrial food comes from and how it's made and all the consequences of buying it, they lose their appetite for eating it. They want food that's fresh, local and organic, that's produced without cruelty and without harming the land. And that's precisely why the organic movement is under attack.

Simple changes in personal behaviour can lead to momentous changes in a political or economic system. You just have to stop supporting the way that things are. Every purchase is like a vote, an endorsement of the supplier and the basic thinking behind the product. Buying food that has been produced the right way, for the right reasons, shifts the marketplace in the right direction. Refusing to buy food that comes from the industrial system weakens that system. But lasting change will require more than ethical, high-minded shopping. So long as money dominates politics, multinational corporations will control the politicians. It's incredible that a handful of corporations in the UK now wield more power than its 60 million citizens. There's no reason that can't change.

When I was born, black and white people in the US couldn't use the same drinking fountains or sleep at the same hotels. During my lifetime I've seen that segregation eliminated from my country, along with the end of apartheid in South Africa, the collapse of the Soviet Union, the fall of the Berlin Wall. These were momentous, systematic changes for the better. And they didn't just happen on their own. Ordinary people made them happen. So when someone tells me that GM crops are inevitable, that factory farms are necessary to produce meat, that we'll always have the Golden Arches, I tell them not to be so sure. Things don't have to be that way, if only enough people want them to be different.

"*We need a set of agricultural practices that seek to work with nature. We need a renewed sense of humility.*"

A SHORT WORD
with Dale Vince

Founder and Managing Director of Ecotricity

HELP TURN ELECTRICITY BILLS INTO WINDMILLS

ECOTRICITY BEGAN IN 1995 WITH THE VERY SINGLE-MINDED MISSION OF CHANGING THE WAY ELECTRICITY IS MADE.

SPECIAL OFFER

Free Annual membership to the Soil Association when you switch to Ecotricity. Please quote *Stuffed* when you call, or sign up online at **www.ecotricity.co.uk/stuffed**, where you can also find out more about our New Energy tariffs and check the prices in your area — we match the standard price of your local supplier.

Terms and conditions apply.

Conventional electricity is the UK's single biggest source of CO_2, so making the switch to green electricity is crucial if we are to avoid the worst effects of climate change. This is our reason for being.

Ecotricity is an electricity company, but with a difference — we take the money our customers spend on their electricity bills and we re-spend it building new sources of clean power — windmills in fact. For every pound our customers pay us we spend another pound building windmills — we like to think of this as turning electricity bills into windmills.

We're recommended by Oxfam and the Soil Association and are the chosen supplier of nearly 40,000 UK homes and businesses, including many involved in food and farming.

We can now all choose who supplies our electricity and where it comes from, so wherever you live in the country you can actually choose to have your home or business supplied by clean energy. The funny thing is, switching takes about five minutes but it's the single biggest thing you can do to fight climate change.

Switching over is easy. You can visit our website and sign up online — **www.ecotricity.co.uk** — or call us on 08000 302 302.

We hope you'll join us.

Dale Vince

RESOURCES AND REFERENCES

Full references and resources are available on the Stuffed website **www.stuffedonline.org**

INTRODUCTION

Church N, 'Why our food is so dependent on oil', Powerswitch (UK), April 2005 www.powerswitch.org.uk

Climate change: Impact on agriculture and costs of adaptation, International Food Policy Research Institute (IFPRI), Washington DC, September 2009

Heinberg R, 'What will we eat as the oil runs out?', Paper presented at the FEASTA Conference, Dublin, Ireland, June 2005

Heller MC and Keoleian GA, 'Life cycle-based sustainability indicators for assessment of the US food system', Ann Arbor, MI: Center for Sustainable Systems, University of Michigan, 2000

Horrigan L, et al, 'How sustainable agriculture can address the environmental and human health harms of industrial agriculture', *Environmental Health Perspectives* 110(5), 2002

Lang, T 'Gardening in an era of food insecurity', Garden Organic President Elect, Speech 50th AGM, September 2008

Reducing the impact of eating, Centre for Alternative Technology, Powys, 2007

Steinfeld H, et al, *Livestock's long shadow: Environmental issues and options,* UN Food and Agriculture Organization (FAO): Rome, Italy, 2006

CHAPTER 01

Checking out the environment: The environmental impacts of supermarkets, Friends of the Earth, June, 2005

Girling R, 'Eat me...and save the planet', *Sunday Times,* July 2009

Rose N et al, 'The 100-mile diet: A community approach to promote sustainable food systems', *Journal of Hunger & Environmental Nutrition,* 3(2), pp 270–85, 2008

Smith A and MacKinnon JB, *The 100-mile diet,* Random House, 2007

Thomas P, 'Behind the eco labels', *Ecologist,* April 2007

What do people want to know about their food? Measuring central coast consumers' interest in food systems issues, The Center for Agroecology & Sustainable Food Systems, University of California, Santa Cruz Research Brief #5, pp 1–4, Winter 2005

Young LR and Nestle M, 'The contribution of expanding portion sizes to US obesity epidemic', *Am J Public Health,* 92, pp 246–49 2002

CHAPTER 02

Clarke A et al, *Living Organic,* Time Life Books, 2001

Dickson Wright C and Scott J, *A Greener Life,* Kyle Cathie, 2009

Gray L, 'Grow your own craze leading to shortages', *Daily Telegraph,* March 28, 2009

Kingsnorth P, 'Acts of Seedition', *Ecologist,* June 2007

Peterkin T, 'Cost of food drives one in three to grow own fruit and veg', *Daily Telegraph,* June 23, 2008

Thomas P, 'Give bees a chance', *Ecologist,* February 2008

CHAPTER 03

Guinness B, 'Landshare schemes: Share and share alike', *Daily Telegraph,* February 2009

Shanin T, 'How the other half lives', *New Scientist* 175(2354): 44 August 3, 2002

Winne M, 'Food Security – It Takes a Community', Center for Ecoliteracy

CHAPTER 04

Website resources for Food for life:
www.foodforlife.org.uk
www.gardenorganic.org.uk
www.healthedtrust.com
www.focusonfood.org

CHAPTER 05

Biggs M, 'An Urban Harvest', *Garden* (Royal Horticultural Society Magazine), October 2009

Growing food in cities, National Food Alliance/SAFE Alliance, June 1996

Growing round the houses: Food production on housing estates, Sustain/Women's Environmental Network, June 2008

Steel C, *Hungry City,* Vintage, 2008

'The abundance handbook: A guide to urban fruit farming', **www.growsheffield.com**

Vidal J, 'City of London plans guerrilla allotments for vacant building sites', *The Guardian,* June 16 2009

CHAPTER 06

Azeez G, 'Soil Carbon and Organic Farming' Soil Association, 2009

Fairlie S, 'Can Britain Feed Itself?' *The Land,* Winter 2007–8

Hamer E, 'Fallow and fertile', *Ecologist,* June 2008

Pearce F, '20-year study backs organic farming', *New Scientist,* May 30, 2002.

Pollan M, 'Farmer in Chief', *New York Times,* October 12, 2008

CHAPTER 07

Agriculture at a crossroads: global report, International Assessment of Agricultural Knowledge, Science and Technology for Development (IAASTD), 2008

Anslow M and Hamer E, '10 Reasons why GM can't feed the world', *Ecologist,* March 2008

Badgley, C et al, *Organic agriculture and the global food supply,* University of Michigan, 2006

Bruges James, 'The biochar debate', Schumacher Briefing no. 16, Schumacher Institute (Bristol), 2009

Hidden Waters, Waterwise Briefing, February 2007
www.waterwise.org.uk

Jones P and Crane R, 'England and Wales under organic agriculture: how much food could be produced?' Centre for Agricultural Strategy, University of Reading, June 2009

Lang T, 'Food Insecurity', *Ecologist* pp 32–34, March 2008

Organic agriculture and biodiversity, International Federation of Organic Agriculture Movements (IFOAM), 2006

Organic agriculture's role in countering climate change, International Federation of Organic Agriculture Movements (IFOAM), 2007

SUGGESTED READING

100-mile diet, The: A year of eating locally
Alisa Smith and JB MacKinnon, Random House, 2007

21st Century is Making you Fat, The
Pat Thomas, Gaia, 2008

Animal, Vegetable, Miracle: Our Year of Seasonal Eating
Barbara Kingsolver, Faber and Faber, 2007

Art of Simple Food, The
Alice Waters, Michael Joseph 2008

Big Earth Book, The
James Bruges, Sawday's Fragile Earth, 2007

Carbon Fields, The
Graham Harvey, Grass Roots, 2008

Dinner Lady, The
Jeanette Orrey and Jamie Oliver, Bantam, 2005

Edible Schoolyard
Alice Waters, Chronicle Books, 2009

Fast Food Nation: What the all-American meal is doing to the World
Eric Schlosser, Penguin, 2002

Feeding People is Easy
Colin Tudge, Pari Publishing, 2007

Food Inc: A Participant Guide – How Industrial Food is Making Us Sicker, Fatter, and Poorer and What You Can Do About it
Karl Weber, Public Affairs, 2009

Food Ward: The Battle for Mouths, Minds and Markets
Tim Lang, Earthscan, 2004

Hungry City
Carolyn Steel, Vintage, 2008

In Defense of Food: An Eater' Manifesto
Michael Pollan, Allen Lane, 2008

Living Dangerously
Pat Thomas, New Leaf, 2003

Money Matters
David Boyle, Sawday's Fragile Earth, 2008

Omnivore's Dilemma, The: A Natural History of Four Meals
Michael Pollan, Bloomsbury, 2007

Party's Over, The
Richard Heinberg, New Society Publishers, 2003

Peak Everything
Richard Heinberg, New Society Publishers, 2008

Shopped: The Shocking Power of British Supermarkets
Joanna Blythman, Harper Perennial, 2005

Stuffed and Starved: Markets, Power and the Hidden Battle for the World Food System
Raj Patel, Portobello, 2008

Transition Handbook, The: From oil dependency to local resilience
Rob Hopkins, Chelsea Green, 2008

What's in this Stuff?
Pat Thomas, Rodale, 2006

We Want Real Food
Graham Harvey, Constable, 2006

USEFUL WEBSITES

Common Ground
www.commonground.org.uk

Friends of the Earth
www.foe.co.uk

Garden Organic
www.gardenorganic.org.uk

Local Exchange Trading Systems (Letslink UK)
www.letslinkuk.org

Local Food Works
www.localfoodworks.org

National Farmers' Retail and Markets Association (FARMA)
www.farmersmarkets.net
www.farma.org.uk

Slow Food
www.slowfood.org.uk

Soil Association
www.soilassociation.org

The Fairtrade Foundation
www.fairtrade.org.uk

The New Economics Foundation
www.neweconomics.org

UK Permaculture Association
www.permaculture.org.uk

WWF
www.wwf.org.uk

PICTURE CREDITS

© Mark Bolton Photography p85

© Ecotricity p186

© ejo photography & design p130

© FFLP p98, 104, 146–147

© FFLP/Terry Rook p50, 102

© Food, INC p78–79

© Istock p24–25, 32, 34–35, 60–61, 74–75, 170–171

© Ken Light p6

© Tricia De Courcy Ling p42

© Low Sizergh Farm p145

© Mark Mann p182

© NTPL/Paul Harris p127

© Stephen Prior p90

© Neil Rees p121

© Soil Association/Sue Gent p174

© Soil Association/Jason Ingram p68

© Soil Association/Charles Sainsbury-Plaice p53, 67, 150

© www.gastroanthropology. com p122–123

INDEX

190

*VOTE WITH YOUR FORK